The expression in Kyle's eyes was so intimate that Corey felt giddy and closed her own eyes. She felt his hand cradle her head beneath the shining curtain of her hair. With his thumb, he lightly traced the outline of her lips, and suddenly she was trembling . . .

"If you win, I'll admit I'm wrong," he promised softly, his voice husky. "That'll be a bonus for you."

"And if *you* win?" she whispered.

"*When* I win, Corey," he corrected her, *warned* her. "When I win, you'll be my bonus."

Dear Reader:

We've had thousands of wonderful surprises at SECOND CHANCE AT LOVE since we launched the line in June 1981.

We knew we were going to have to work hard to bring you the six best romances we could each month. We knew we were working with a talented, caring group of authors. But we *didn't* know we were going to receive such a warm and generous response from readers. So the thousands of wonderful surprises are in the form of letters from readers like you who've been kind with your praise, constructive and helpful with your suggestions. We read each letter...and take it seriously.

It's been a thrill to ''meet'' our readers, to discover that the people who read SECOND CHANCE AT LOVE novels and write to us about them are so remarkable. Our romances can only get better and better as we learn more and more about you, the reader, and what you like to read.

So, I hope you will continue to enjoy SECOND CHANCE AT LOVE and, if you haven't written to us before, please feel free to do so. If you have written, keep in touch.

With every good wish,

SECOND CHANCE AT LOVE Staff
The Berkley/Jove Publishing Group
200 Madison Avenue
New York, New York 10016

VENUS RISING

MICHELLE ROLAND

A
SECOND CHANCE AT LOVE
BOOK

VENUS RISING

CHAPTER
One

COREY KENYON'S HOROSCOPE for that day read, "Due
to the increasingly strong influence of Venus, romance
will figure more prominently in your life than ever before."

Corey followed her horoscope out of habit; she didn't
attach much significance to astrology, and she certainly
didn't waste any time waiting around for the events it
forecast to come true. So when her half sister, Janet,
phoned to ask if she could come over to her apartment
after work, Corey didn't look for any connection between
this event and her daily horoscope. There was nothing
remarkable about Jan's call except that it was unlike her
to stand on ceremony or to give much consideration to
the convenience of others.

Even when Corey got home from work and found that
Janet's boyfriend, Andrew Zachary, was waiting there
with Jan, who had her own key, the only unusual thing
Corey noticed was that Drew had risen attentively to his
feet when she'd come into the living room. But this was
not the first time she'd been struck by the discordant
contrast between Drew's flawless courtesy and his student's guise of ragged jeans and faded khaki shirt.

Drew Zachary was working toward his doctorate in
mathematics at the Madison campus of the University
of Wisconsin.

1

On weekends Drew indulged his passion for music by playing clarinet with a jazz ensemble at various local nightclubs. It was at one of these club dates almost a year before that Janet had met him. In the beginning they had dated casually, but in the past six months they'd become inseparable, spending practically all their free time together.

At first Corey had worried about Jan seeing so much of Drew, but the tendency to worry about her young half sister was another unfortunate—and unproductive—habit she'd developed. In her heart Corey knew it was an exercise in futility to worry about Jan!

She'd come to like Drew. Once she'd gotten around his affectations of dress and his militant disdain for any kind of monetary considerations, she had reached the conclusion that he was basically a well-intentioned boy. And, she acknowledged, he was *only* a boy. While he was actually less than two years younger than her own twenty-six, most of the time his behavior was as inconsistent as eighteen-year-old Jan's. One minute he was the mature adult, the next he was gleefully adolescent.

Corey thought his relative immaturity was partially due to the fact that he was still in school and hadn't yet been required to come to terms with the real world outside the ivory tower of the university. Since she didn't believe that most students were so impractical, this suggested that Drew must have been sheltered from life's more prosaic concerns in some way, but Corey had never pursued this puzzle. With his dark, wildly curling hair and full beard, it was a little difficult to make out his features clearly, but there was no doubt he was attractive. She especially admired the way he'd handled Jan's mother, Vera.

Surprisingly in view of the emphasis Vera placed on wealth and good grooming, Drew had won her over to the extent that she'd begun to actively approve of him. She had even encouraged Jan to see him to the exclusion of other boys. It was possible, however, that this was only a ploy to reduce the friction between herself and her daughter. They'd fought strenuously over almost everything since Jan had reached her teens.

Even as she wondered about why Vera had such a positive attitude toward Drew, Corey came farther into the living room, said her hello's to Janet and Drew, and sank into one of the chairs facing the sofa.

Drew took Jan's hand in his and as they stared at Corey, their expressions were identically grave.

"The two of you look awfully serious," Corey observed uneasily. "What is it you want to talk to me about?"

Jan and Drew exchanged a conspiratorial look. Giving Jan's hand a reassuring squeeze, Drew announced, "We want to get married."

His tone was quarrelsome, and Jan mirrored his defiance with the mutinous tilt of her chin as she confirmed, "Yes, we do."

For a few seconds, Corey studied the couple silently, asking herself why she hadn't seen this coming. Aloud she said dryly, "You seem to be expecting me to try to talk you out of it. Do you want someone who's been there to debate the pros and cons with you, or are you simply keeping me informed?"

Drew grinned apologetically and, smiling a little shakily, Jan said, "You're the only one we've told so far. Actually, we'd like your help."

"My help?" Corey echoed uncertainly, looking from her sister to Drew and back.

"I don't expect Mother to object," said Jan. "It's Drew's family that'll take some persuading."

"Back up a bit," Corey pleaded. "I'm still trying to get used to the idea of you two being engaged! And you are a little young to be considering marriage, Jan. How can you be so sure that Vera won't object?"

"Because Mother's known from the start that Drew is one of *the* Zacharys."

Corey stared at her sister, uncomprehending, and Jan exclaimed impatiently, "You know—Zachary Electronics!"

Corey's amazed glance flew in Drew's direction. Naturally she'd heard of Zachary Electronics. In the past decade the Chicago-based firm had developed so many computer components, as well as different models of calculators and more common types of office machines, it had become virtually a household name. But she'd never connected Drew with that family. The way he dressed, the rusted and battered old Volkswagen he drove—nothing of his life style gave any evidence that his background was a wealthy one.

"Take my word for it," Jan said smugly, "Mother will be delighted."

"The one we'd like your help with is my brother, Kyle," Drew said quickly. "He's the mover and shaker, the holder of the family purse-strings, and he's already agreed, in principle, to my asking Jan to marry me."

"Where's your problem then?" Corey inquired, more baffled than before.

"When I discussed our engagement with Kyle, he said I'm of age and so is Jan, so it's up to us. *But* he believes a married man should be self-supporting. In other words, since I'm a year away from my degree, I'll have to drop out of school unless we can convince Kyle to change his mind and continue to help out financially after the wedding."

Sighing, Drew slumped against the back of the couch. "I barely clear enough playing with the band weekends for pin money, and with my class schedule it's unlikely I'll be able to find a part-time job that would allow me to earn my own way. My academic standing is good enough that I expect the university to come through with a fellowship this fall, but that's still not going to pay enough to provide for a wife and family."

The silence that followed Drew's statement was electric.

"Family?" Corey repeated faintly, stunned by the implications of the word.

"Drew, did anyone ever tell you you've got a big

mouth? Why don't you just hire a hall?" Jan cried sarcastically. Turning anxiously to Corey, she said, "I was going to tell you, but not quite so bluntly. You're the first to know this, too. We plan to wait to tell Mom she's going to have a grandchild until we've been married a month or so. The way I figure it, the very thought of being a grandmother is going to send her into such a tailspin that she'll never even notice the time element."

"You're pregnant?"

Jan nodded. Her face was flushed and her blue eyes were suspiciously bright.

"Are you sure, honey?" Corey asked gently.

"Of course, I'm sure. I wasn't born yesterday, you know! The doctor confirmed our suspicions today. I swear I was going to tell you myself. That's why Drew came with me to see you, to give me moral support—" She stopped speaking abruptly and giggled, but her laughter was brittle and edged with hysteria. "Oh, God! It's such a bad pun! *Moral* support. Get it?"

In an effort to calm Jan, Drew curved his arm protectively about her shoulders and patted her, while Corey hurriedly asked, "What is it you'd like me to do?"

"Kyle is going to be in Madison tomorrow night," Drew replied, "and we need some place to meet with him privately, on neutral ground."

"*Not* at my house," Jan inserted vehemently, "because if Kyle gets one look at my mother, that'll convince him that his worst fears are being realized and all I'm interested in is the Zachary money. And we can't talk to him at Drew's place because his roommates are throwing a going-away party for a friend."

"So you'd like to meet him here."

In unison, the two on the couch nodded.

"When do you plan to get married?"

"The sooner the better—a week or two at most. If we can't talk Kyle into continuing my allowance, we'll just have to work out some other way. I'll have to drop out of school temporarily, or something. Jan's offered to work, but we can't expect her to be able to contribute much financially. She hasn't had any training or experience."

Drew had answered without hesitation, but he had refused to meet Corey's eyes. Although she was favorably impressed that his attitude toward the problem of finances was hardly his usual radical tirade on the subject, she felt forced to ask, "Are you both very certain that you want to get married?"

"Of course we are," Jan said hotly. "If we weren't sure of that, we wouldn't be here now."

"I want to marry Jan more than I can say," Drew said in an even tone. "It's the unpleasantness with my brother that I dread. Lord!" He groaned. "I can just imagine what Kyle will say."

"Is he such an ogre?"

"No!" Jan shook her head in vigorous denial. "He's incredibly attractive and charming. After seeing him, it's a mystery to me where he ever got the notion that women are only after his money. I mean, he's so sexy, I don't think most women would care if he didn't have a cent, they'd still find him exciting."

"You've only met him briefly, Jan, so you haven't seen him do his boardroom number," Drew said. "I wouldn't go so far as to say he's an ogre, Corey, but Kyle can be a helluva tough customer, and once he's reached a final decision, it might as well be chiseled in granite." To emphasize the point, Drew pounded his closed fist into the palm of his other hand.

"As to his ideas about the mercenary qualities of women, in a way it's no wonder he feels the way he does. Our mother died when I was born, and in the next twelve years he watched our father go through three wives. All of them looked great at first, and all of them turned out to be primarily concerned with feathering their nests. By the time Dad paid off the last one to get rid of her, he was almost bankrupt and he was so despondent he took a dive out of the window of his office." Drew grimaced. "It happened to be on the fourteenth floor, and

Kyle had to identify the remains."

"Something like that would leave a mark on anyone," Jan said in a subdued voice.

"Yeah," Drew agreed. "Outwardly, though, Kyle never turned a hair. He was barely out of college himself, but he stepped in and took over a rundown factory that had manufactured radios and televisions and parlayed it into the diversified, highly successful corporation it is today."

It was apparent to Corey that despite his attempted nonchalance, Drew harbored considerable admiration for his older brother's "cool."

"Kyle must have had women in his life," Jan insisted. "With his looks and aura of power, he'd have to be a target for all kinds."

"I never claimed he was a monk," Drew countered. "Kyle has all the normal masculine drives, but he loves 'em and leaves 'em. He uses women and throws them away and somehow or other, in spite of his reputation, they keep lining up for the privilege of being next. I guess he has a certain fascination for the ladies. Each one probably tells herself that she'll be the one to change him."

He shook his head, incapable of understanding such foolishness. "What is it with you women that you find a man like Kyle so devastating? Women seem to take one look at him and lose whatever common sense they have."

"As you just said, Drew," Jan replied, "he's fascinating. He presents a challenge to a girl's femininity. They think, 'if a man like that wants me, that's proof I must be extremely desirable.'"

Drew frowned, pretending sternness. "I can see I'm going to have to prevent your seeing much of Kyle after we're married. You show all the classic signs of falling for his fatal attraction."

"Ah, sweetheart, I was only talking theoretically." Jan's expression was stricken. "You know I love you."

"Yeah, babe, I know," Drew said softly.

He obviously believed her and, seeing Jan's adoring smile, so did Corey. They seemed lost in one another for the moment and unaware of her presence. She cleared her throat as a discreet reminder they were not alone and they turned to face her expectantly.

"You can meet Kyle here," she said. "What time are you planning to see him?"

"Not till about seven o'clock," Jan said, sagging with relief into the circle of Drew's arm.

"I'll spend the evening with my neighbor across the hall," Corey said. "You can just knock on her door when you've finished."

"I thought you might be persuaded to join us. After all you've heard about Kyle, aren't you just dying to meet him?" Jan asked. "Besides, I want to make a good impression on him—at least as good as possible—and Drew agrees with me that you're the very image of virtue and incorruptibility."

Corey felt her cheeks grow warm as she sat tongue-tied, searching for a tactful answer. She didn't want to offend Drew, but her impulse was to avoid meeting his brother. She was grateful when Drew saved her by speaking up.

"I think Corey would be smart to make herself scarce. If Kyle were to meet her, it wouldn't be her sterling character that would impress him! No, babe," he insisted firmly when Jan looked like she wanted to push the point. "I'm very fond of our lovely Corey, and I wouldn't bring her to my big brother's attention for anything in the world. It would be like throwing a lamb to a wolf!"

As she drove home the following day, Corey had plenty of time to think about the meeting that was to take place in a little less than two hours' time between Kyle Zachary, Drew, and Jan. While her job as executive secretary to a group of attorneys was on the east side of Capitol Square, her apartment was on the far west side of Madison. This meant that she had to pass through the bottleneck of "the Isthmus" in her commute to and from work. On this Friday afternoon, the drive was even more time-consuming and nerve-frazzling than usual because of the traffic caused by a bus drivers' strike.

While Corey was caught in the bumper-to-bumper line of cars winding its way around the capitol building, she told herself that if Drew could hear her now, he'd be shocked to learn how wrong he'd been in comparing her to a lamb. There was nothing at all gentle about the epithets she muttered in her private commentary on the kamikaze tactics of some of the other drivers. And the bicycle riders! And the pedestrians! It was one of those days when they seemed to be converging from every direction to hurl themselves, like so many lemmings, into the snarled sea of traffic bound for University Avenue.

Although Corey was blessed with a dancer's lissome slenderness and her face was saved from cold perfection by the sauciness of her turned-up nose, she was so unassuming that her near-beauty often went unnoticed. Because of Vera she had learned at a very early age to make herself as inconspicuous as possible in order to minimize her stepmother's disapproval. But through it all, Corey had kept her courage, her spunkiness. She didn't give in easily to the demands of others.

Still, it didn't occur to her that Drew hadn't referred to her as a lamb because he considered her so mild or docile, but because of the suggestion of softness about her that reminded him of a lamb. Her fine-spun golden-brown hair, the generous fullness of her mouth, her silky skin with its summer tan that came close to being the same sunkissed shade as her hair, the sweet curves of her body—all gave the impression of being intensely soft and touchable.

Since he'd never been one to mince words, Drew had said as much to Corey. Within minutes of their first meeting, he'd told her, "You look so damned cuddly! There's something about you that has the same effect on me as a kitten and makes me want to pet you."

"Braver men than you have tried, my lad," Corey had

laughingly paraphrased in return. "A few have felt they were called, but *none* were chosen."

Corey knew Jan had told Drew she'd once been married, and she wasn't surprised by the open astonishment he showed at her remark. "Not even your ex-husband?" he'd asked.

Thoughts about her brief, unhappy marriage, made Corey's smile fade. In a tone that made it clear the discussion was closed, she replied, "Not even Lance."

She might have put it much more strongly and said, *"Especially* not Lance," for he had never really shown her any tenderness.

Corey was barely seventeen when she met Lance Gilchrist, and not much older when they eloped. He had put on such a convincing show of concern—declaring how desperately he wanted to take care of her, moaning that it would be years before he'd be in a position to support a wife. Corey was completely taken in. By the time she'd realized that Lance hadn't been particularly attentive until after he'd found out about the nest egg her mother had left her, it was too late.

Her father had died only a few months before and she was so pathetically hungry for affection, so eager to escape her stepmother's clutches, that she'd been ripe for Lance's deceptions. She had been deplorably easy to fool. She had mistaken Lance's sexual demands for love, his soft-spoken manner for gentleness, his greed for ambition.

Corey had been so infatuated that marriage to Lance had seemed the solution to all her troubles. Since money was the only thing keeping them apart, she had explained to him that while her inheritance was tied up in a trust and, under the conditions of her father's will, control of the trust had passed to her stepmother, her marriage would allow her to claim the funds. That was when Lance had suggested they elope.

But Vera's greed was as great as Lance's and her power had far outweighed his. Corey had finally learned how firmly her husband kept his eye on the main chance when Vera threatened to file statutory rape charges against him unless he was willing to accept a cash settlement and permit the marriage to be set aside. Lance had agreed to an annulment with unflattering haste. Afterward he'd simply taken the money and run, and Corey hadn't seen or heard from him since.

In the end, it was Vera who walked away with all the marbles. Not only had she had the pleasure of showing Corey how little their marriage meant to Lance, she'd won the admiration of her friends for her decisive actions.

Vera had also kept control of the trust, and because of business reversals and her uninspired management, by the time Corey reached the age of twenty-one, her inheritance had dwindled to a few thousand dollars. But that had been enough to buy her freedom. She had moved into her own apartment, and in the last five years she had returned to her stepmother's home very rarely, and then only to see Jan.

Getting over Lance hadn't been as easy. Although she hardly ever thought about him these days, in some ways she still hadn't fully recovered. Now and again something would jog her memory, as Drew's question had, and it would all come back, so vividly, so painfully, it was as if it had all happened yesterday.

When Drew and Jan had dropped her at her apartment later that evening, she'd known she was in for a sleepless night, and when she'd confronted herself in the mirror the next morning, she'd wondered how she could look so fresh and bright and unscarred.

There were times when she resented her youthful appearance, and that had been one of them. It seemed only fair that she should have something tangible to show for her grief, and if it had to be circles under her eyes, or a few lines in her face, or even a generally ravaged look, so be it. But surely she deserved *something*.

It had soon become obvious to Corey that her reticence about her marriage had served only to pique Drew's curiosity. Later that morning Jan had phoned to ask her to try to be less standoffish with Drew the next time she saw him.

With a bluntness that was tolerable only because she hadn't the least idea how hurtful her honesty could be, Jan had said, "You were so cool, Drew thought you didn't like him. He even asked me if you have something against men, but I told him that it was more likely you feel threatened if *anyone* gets too close."

Cringing at this invasion of her privacy, Corey had asked, "What else did you tell Drew?"

"I tried to explain, naturally. I told him that my mother has always been harsh with you because you have the misfortune of resembling Laura, and that Mom is absolutely rabid on the subject of Daddy's first wife."

"Anything else?"

"If you must know, I told him the whole sad story about how Daddy stopped paying any attention at all to you, hoping that would encourage Mom to ease up a bit, and how you'd always kept your nose buried in a book after that."

"Jan!" Corey exploded. "How could you?"

"Well, it's the truth, Corey. Anyone can see that ever since the disaster with Lance Gilchrist you prefer imaginary characters to people. I guess it must be because you've found most people are unreliable, not to mention unpredictable and uncontrollable."

At Corey's gasp of outrage, Jan hastened to add, "Don't get me wrong. It's not that I don't sympathize with you, and I can certainly understand the reasoning behind it."

Jan's analysis was accurate as far as it went, but by no means was it the whole story, for Corey wasn't strictly a spectator in life. She had allowed a select few to infiltrate the barrier of reserve that kept most people at bay, and once she'd given her affection, she was unswerving in her loyalty.

She couldn't be otherwise. The death of her mother, the defection of her father, and the desertion of her husband had taught her how important it was to stand by a friend.

It wasn't the betrayal of others Corey feared, nor was it that others were uncontrollable. What she feared was losing control of herself. Her greatest fear was that she would be betrayed by her own passionate nature, for she knew that once she had given her love, she could never bring herself to withdraw it.

Because she sensed that the depth of her own commitment left her peculiarly vulnerable, with most people she tried to maintain a certain amount of remoteness. Jan was one of those for whom Corey had made an exception. She also had a few friends, and they were close and steadfast. Lorraine Bishop, the neighbor she planned to visit that evening, was in this category. They'd been friends since their first day in kindergarten.

Corey's lips curved in anticipation of a pleasant evening. The smile animated her face, causing the young man driving the delivery van in the lane of cars next to hers to stare at her with admiration and try to catch her eye.

But the light turned green again just then and, seeing an opening in the faster moving traffic in the express lane, Corey adeptly swerved her small car into it and quickly disappeared.

CHAPTER

Two

THE TELEPHONE BEGAN ringing just as Corey stepped into the shower.

"Never known it to fail," she muttered as she turned off the water and reached for her towel.

She wrapped the towel around herself and trailed wetly down the hall and through the living room to the kitchen. Just as she lifted the receiver, the caller hung up and all she heard was the empty hum of an open line followed by the monotonous burr of the dial tone.

"I wonder who that was," she murmured, looking at the receiver as though it might answer her question. Then she shrugged. If it was important, whoever it was would try again. But not, she hoped, before she'd finished her shower.

The day had been another hot and muggy one, typical of late June in Wisconsin, and her apartment had been like a sauna when she'd gotten home. On her way back to the bathroom, she stopped to turn the thermostat controlling the air conditioner to a lower setting, shivering with pleasure in the direct blast of its icy breath. By the time Jan, Drew, and his brother, Kyle, arrived, the place should be comfortably cooled.

This thought caused her to retrace the path of damp tracks she'd made very quickly so she could complete her shower with time to spare before Kyle Zachary arrived.

Corey had reentered the bathroom when she realized that if, for once, Jan should happen to be on time, she'd have to go through the whole dripping procedure again. Giving herself a mental pat on the back for taking care of this contingency, she turned back along the hall to the living room where she released the chain on the front door so her sister could let herself in with her key. Certain she wouldn't be interrupted again, she returned to the bathroom.

Because her shoulder-length hair felt sticky and the tepid spray of the shower was so refreshing, she decided on a shampoo. She'd barely finished rinsing when the doorbell rang.

"Oh, no!" she groaned. Could Jan have forgotten her key?

Again the doorbell sounded, with the same strangely imperious urgency as was sometimes the case with a long-distance telephone call. Jan *must* have forgotten her key.

This time Corey took long enough to wrap the towel around her hair and secure a bath sheet saronglike about herself. She left the bathroom, thinking longingly of the cool, leisurely shower whose time apparently had not yet come. As she padded barefoot across the gold shag carpeting in the living room, she tried to decide whether she would have enough time to run the vacuum and destroy the evidence of her interrupted shower. Its story was plainly told in all the damp footprints she'd left to mar the otherwise pristine surface of the carpet.

The doorbell rang again.

"Oh, Lord!" she cried. "I'm coming." Even as she was opening the door, she exclaimed, "For pity's sake, Jan, what's the rush?"

She had opened the door only a fraction when she saw the tall, dark-haired man who waited outside. He towered over her, and it seemed as if she had to look up an awfully long way before she finally glimpsed his face—dark, piratical, and somehow frightening. Quickly she hitched the slipping towel more securely over her breasts.

"You're not Janet," she accused as she leaped behind the door and leaned against it in an effort to close it.

"Obviously," the man drawled. "And neither are you."

She was too late. He'd pushed one expensively shod foot into the opening. She peered at him through the crack at the hinged edge of the door.

His impeccably tailored, light-gray summer-weight suit also looked costly, as did his white-on-white patterned shirt, and silk burgundy and navy necktie. She wouldn't risk another look at his face, and her frantic gaze settled on the leather attaché case he held in one lean hand. Weren't stripes of that color the Gucci trademark? Whether they were or not, everything about the man whispered "money." Was he a salesman? Unlikely, but it was a possibility. Hadn't she read somewhere that salesmen have the highest earning ratio of any occupation?

From behind the concealment of the door, she called optimistically, "I'm not interested in buying anything."

"That's just as well, because I'm not selling anything. But if *you* are, I'd be very interested in buying."

The man's voice was deep-toned and suggestive, and Corey panicked and threw all her weight against the door, straining mightily and panting in her effort before she conceded that it was futile. She couldn't budge him.

"Please let go of the door," she gasped.

"Certainly," he replied equably. "After you let me in."

"If you don't let me close the door this instant," she threatened shakily, "I'll scream."

"Don't make a bigger fool of yourself than you already have," he said softly. He sounded weary, as if he were growing bored with the situation. "I'm Kyle Zachary and I believe I'm expected."

As if to emphasize her dismay, the telephone started

to ring. Corey stood frozen behind the door, her mind scrambling for a way to make a dignified retreat from the embarrassing scene.

"I know you're still there," Kyle remarked dryly. "I can hear you breathing."

Oh God! Corey silently asked. What did I ever do to deserve this?

"Why don't you go into your room and get dressed," he suggested evenly, "while I answer the phone."

When Corey still gave no indication as to her decision, he prompted her. "Well? I promise not to peek."

"A-all right," she agreed breathlessly.

Before she could reconsider, she left the illusory haven of the door and rushed headlong in the direction of her bedroom. Before she got there, though, she heard her visitor chuckling behind her. She was so incensed by his unfeeling enjoyment of her predicament that she didn't even notice that the phone had stopped ringing. She wheeled to confront him, daring to look directly at his face for the first time.

Beneath well-defined brows his eyes flashed with humor, and his strong teeth gleamed whitely against his deeply tanned skin. If his clothing hinted of money, everything about his ruggedly handsome face shouted strength and confidence. Even the crisp, vital way his hair curled about his broad forehead and the austere planes of his temples spoke of dynamism; proclaimed that here was a man who was completely aware of his power and who would not hesitate to use it to his own advantage.

Corey was riveted by his gaze and impotently enraged. Her eyes were so stormy that their velvety blue appeared almost black in the delicate oval of her face. "Since you find this so funny, I wonder what you do when you set out to have a good time," she fumed irately. "Pull the wings off butterflies? Steal candy from babies?"

Kyle's grin only broadened. His dark eyes danced as they ruthlessly explored the outline of her body.

"I hate to have to tell you this," he said mildly, "but

you're about to lose your modesty."

As she frantically tugged the slipping towel higher, turned and fled to the privacy of her room, Corey felt stung from the tips of her toes to the roots of her hair. Infuriated, she slammed the door behind herself before she collapsed onto the side of the bed. She remained huddled on the edge of the mattress, trembling with re-action even when she heard the phone ring. Kyle knocked on the door a few minutes later.

"Corey," he called softly. "At least I hope you're Corey!" He chuckled once more. "That telephone call just now was from Drew. He only wanted to warn you about my early arrival."

She whipped into action then and hurriedly pulled on the clean clothing she'd laid out before her shower—the wisps of underwear, the white terry cloth jogging shorts, and navy-and-white striped tank top. She'd just slipped into her thonged sandals when the telephone rang again. This time, however, it was soon silenced.

Impulsively, Corey grabbed up her purse and let her-self out of the bedroom. It seemed to her a stroke of good fortune when she found the hallway empty and the living room deserted. Apparently Kyle was still in the kitchen talking on the phone. Stealthily she opened the front door and stepped into the corridor of the apartment building, breathing a sigh of relief at the success of her escape when she'd closed the door soundlessly behind her.

"But what's the point of your sneaking out like that, Corey?" Lorraine asked sometime later, her forehead creased with perplexity.

They were in Lorraine's kitchen and Corey was perched on a stool at the breakfast bar watching her friend as she prepared spaghetti sauce for their dinner. Lorraine had greeted Corey with astonishment when she'd arrived at her door, white-lipped with tension and with her freshly washed hair still swathed in the towel. Once Corey had taken up Lorraine's offer of the loan of her hair dryer, it was obvious she had some explaining to do. She'd had no choice but to tell Lorraine about Kyle's unexpected appearance and how embarrassing it had been.

"What I mean is," Lorraine continued, "with Jan and Drew getting married, he'll be Jan's brother-in-law. You're bound to have to see him occasionally."

"I know it was silly of me," Corey said, "but I just couldn't face him again tonight."

"He's terribly good-looking."

"You saw him?"

Lorraine nodded. "He arrived just as I was coming home from work and he followed me into the building." Reluctantly she admitted, "I even held the door for him and directed him to your apartment."

"Honestly!" Corey exclaimed. "What's the use of living in a security-locked building if people aren't more careful about letting strangers in?"

"I know I shouldn't have done it," Lorraine apologized hastily. "It's just—well, he smiled at me so nicely. And you have to admit he's not a a burglar or a sex fiend or anything like that. He's an extremely respectable businessman."

"I agree I won't have to count the pennies in my piggy bank or worry he'll steal the silverware, but while he's probably respected, I doubt he's any more respectable than he has to be. The 'sex fiend' part, I'm not at all sure of!"

"I'm sorry, Corey."

Lorraine appeared to be genuinely contrite, and Corey sighed. "It's really not your fault. I'd have had to let him in anyway. I'm more angry at myself than anyone else."

Her friend looked at her quizzically.

"Jan wanted so much to make a good impression on Kyle, and Drew hoped to convince him to continue paying him an allowance after they're married," Corey explained dejectedly. "I don't think my behavior has helped their cause. I only hope I haven't completely sabotaged it."

"I'm sure you haven't." Lorraine offered this encouragement absently as she sampled the sauce she'd been stirring. "Hmmm," she murmured thoughtfully, holding out the partially filled spoon with her free hand cupped beneath it to catch any spills. "Taste this and tell me what you think."

Corey tasted the sauce. "Maybe a little more oregano," she suggested.

Lorraine considered this briefly. "I think you're right," she agreed, measuring more of the herb into the rich tomato-y sauce.

"Isn't that an awfully big batch you're making?"

Lorraine smiled. "Nate's coming for dinner tonight, too."

At this reference to Lorraine's fiance, Nathan Lund, Corey slid off the stool to her feet. "Why didn't you tell me sooner? The two of you will want to be alone. I'll go out somewhere—to a movie or something."

"Nonsense! I won't hear of it. Anyway, Nate and I have gone beyond the stage of petting and kissing in corners."

"Oh?" Corey teased. "Since when?"

"Since we decided to be married," Lorraine replied evenly, leaving Corey to draw her own conclusions as to the exact meaning of her reponse. "You're staying," Lorraine declared firmly. "In fact, you can make yourself useful by fixing the salad for me."

In spite of her protests that she had no desire to be a fifth wheel, a few minutes later Corey found herself installed at the counter preparing the crisped lettuce and slicing the other salad vegetables into a large wooden bowl while Lorraine went through the cupboards, assembling the ingredients for the dressing. From the increasingly hectic quality of her searching, it became evident that there was something missing.

Finally, she muttered, "Darn it, I can't find the vinegar. I must have forgotten to buy more."

"I'll go out and get some," Corey offered.

"Would you?" Lorraine smiled in relief as she pushed

a lock of seal-brown hair back from one cheek. "I'd go myself, but Nate should be here any second."

There was a supermarket only a few blocks away, and Corey elected to walk rather than drive that short distance. Besides giving her time to think, it would give Nate and Lorraine at least a few minutes alone. They were planning to be married in the fall, when Nate had finished his residency in obstetrics and gynecology at the university hospital, but in the meantime the demands of his work schedule were such that they had very little time together.

Although the sun was setting with an extravagantly fiery display of crimson, orange, and rose, it was still oppressively hot. Corey lingered for a time in the welcome chilliness of the store, browsing through the magazines and racks of paperback books.

As she strolled back toward Lorraine's through the blue-gray light of the gathering dusk, she castigated herself for behaving so irrationally. She had an unopened bottle of tarragon vinegar in her own kitchen. The sensible thing to do would have been to collect that, spend some time in the comfort of her own living room, and, incidentally, make her peace with Kyle Zachary.

Drat the man, anyway! Why should she have this hesitancy—face it, Corey, she told herself sternly—this *fear* of seeing him? She felt her body tensing at the mere memory of his supremely self-confident, darkly handsome face.

She'd never reacted so violently to anyone before. She tried to convince herself that she had this compulsion to keep her distance simply because he'd laughed at her farcical handling of their meeting. But buried deep inside was the knowledge that she had instinctively wanted to run from Kyle the first moment she'd seen him outside her door.

"Look who's here, Corey," Lorraine caroled gaily as she let her into the apartment a few minutes later.

Corey's eyes slanted past her friend to the center of the living room where Kyle stood beside Nathan Lund. His head was inclined toward Nate, who was shorter than he by several inches. One hand was hooked into the pocket of his slacks while the other held a wine glass. But he was looking at *her,* and his expression contradicted his casual stance as their glances met and locked.

"Isn't this a nice surprise?" Lorraine's hazel eyes were sparkling and her cheeks were flushed with excitement. "At the last minute, it turned out that Drew's jazz band had a booking tonight and he had to break up their meeting early, so I invited Kyle to join us for dinner. He was leaving just as Nate arrived. Isn't that a lucky coincidence?"

In that instant, Corey could have cheerfully throttled her friend, but for the life of her she couldn't speak. Her tongue seemed to be fused to the roof of her mouth, rendering her mute as Lorraine ushered her into the room, relieved her of her grocery parcel, and disappeared into the kitchen.

"Hi, Corey," Nate greeted her warmly. "How about some wine?" He gestured with the hand that was holding his own half-filled glass. "We're all one up on you. I can't vouch for the vintage, and I'll warn you it's not a corked bottle, but it doesn't taste half bad after the first glass."

Without waiting for her reply, Nate turned to pour some burgundy for her from the bottle on the cocktail table and, with nerveless fingers, she accepted the glass he held out to her.

"More for you, Kyle?" Nate asked, waving the bottle in his direction.

"Yes, thanks." Even as he held out his glass for a refill, Kyle's unwavering assessment of her continued. If anything, it became more piercing, and Corey felt her cheeks stinging with the heat of the self-conscious color that flooded into them.

"I think I'll see if Lorraine needs any help," she excused herself in a strangled voice and all but ran from the living room where Kyle responded to her confusion with a knowing smile.

In the kitchen she found Lorraine was putting the finishing touches on a dainty bouquet of roses and baby's breath at the center of the small table that was set for four.

"There," she said, stepping back and surveying her handiwork with satisfaction. "I think it looks very nice, don't you?"

"Yes, it does," Corey agreed flatly, "but I can't stay."

"Why ever in the world not?"

"Didn't you listen to anything I said earlier tonight?"

"Of course I did," Lorraine assured her in lowered tones, "and it seems to me that this is the perfect opportunity for you to make amends for the way you acted earlier."

In the face of such topsy-turvy logic, Corey was speechless.

"Anyway, I think Kyle is very charming. *He* certainly doesn't seem to bear any grudges."

"He has no reason to," Corey retorted in an impassioned whisper. "I'm the one who was humiliated, not him." She glanced deprecatingly at her shorts and shirt. "Besides, I'm not dressed appropriately."

"Well, if that's all that's bothering you, go on and change."

Corey was surprised by Lorraine's apparent inability to appreciate the basic problem, which was that she didn't *want* to have dinner with Kyle Zachary. She wanted nothing whatsoever to do with him. The argument regarding her casual style of dress was only a smokescreen that Lorraine would ordinarily have recognized for the ruse it was.

"If you want to change your clothes, for heaven's sake hurry up and do it," Lorraine urged her impatiently. "Dinner will be ready in a few minutes."

* * *

In her own apartment, Corey was mindful of Kyle's disconcerting boldness during his visual exploration of her body, and she gave some consideration to her wardrobe before making a selection. As she exchanged her abbreviated shorts and T-shirt for an all-enveloping caftan of gossamer-fine turquoise and cream cotton lawn, she wondered how Kyle had been able to cast his spell over Lorraine so quickly.

She would have thought her friend's engagement to Nate would offer her *some* protection, but evidently it hadn't. It appeared that Lorraine had succumbed to Kyle Zachary's wiles and was unusually insensitive to Corey's feelings. She was practically forcing Corey to spend the evening in the company of a man Corey fervently wished to avoid and at this point, if she didn't have dinner with them she'd seem inexcusably rude. Neither alternative was acceptable, but when she thought of Jan and Drew, she was left with no choice. She'd just have to grin and bear it.

Corey had brushed her hair until it followed the curve of her neck and lay like a satiny cape about her slender shoulders. The golden-brown shimmer of it was highlighted by occasional sunbleached streaks. It had a tendency to curl unmanageably in the humid summer weather, and she knew that before the evening was over the sleek style would be ruined. With a sigh, she fastened some fine gold hoops in her earlobes and smoothed on lip gloss in a muted coral shade before she appraised her appearance in the mirror.

The loose-fitting fabric of the caftan was lightweight and cool though it clung strategically to the gentle contours of her body, but she was in no mood to recognize the unique loveliness she possessed. She felt strangely victimized. She had a growing conviction that Kyle had cleverly maneuvered her into tonight's dinner and that he now had her precisely where he wanted her. And all she could do was wait for the other shoe to drop—wait helplessly for the purpose that lay behind his machinations to be revealed.

CHAPTER
Three

BOTH JAN AND Lorraine had called Kyle "charming," and the adjective was certainly accurate, Corey thought somewhat sourly as she observed him at the candlelit dinner table. She resented the ease with which he was now turning his charm on Nate, who seemed to find Kyle very likable indeed, despite the fact that Lorraine could hardly take her eyes off him.

Kyle listened with flattering attentiveness to whichever of Corey's friends happened to be talking during the meal. He drew them out and seemed truly interested in each of them. At first Corey thought it was all an act. As the evening wore on, however, she became less convinced that this was so, for he gave the consistent appearance of enjoying himself immensely. Even *he* couldn't be that accomplished an actor.

Maybe the casualness of the dinner party was a pleasant change from the formality of the dinners to which he was accustomed. She'd had no experience with such high-powered company as he must ordinarily keep, and she couldn't envision in detail what differences there might be, but she was sure that this was hardly his usual milieu.

At last the meal ended. Sighing contentedly, Lorraine

pushed her chair away from the table, rose, and began collecting the dessert dishes.

"Let me give you a hand," Corey offered hurriedly, breaking the long silence that had been her refuge.

"Nothing doing, Corey," Nate said firmly. "I'll help Lorraine with the dishes. Why don't you and Kyle go on into the living room?"

She didn't want to intrude further on Lorraine and Nate's privacy, so she followed Kyle into the living room. He relaxed on the sofa, loosening his tie and stretching his long legs out before him, while she sat stiffly in the chair farthest from him. Though she'd been forced into being alone with him, at least the distance was an improvement over the cozy confines of the dinner table, which was so small that his knee had occasionally brushed hers.

"You're very quiet," Kyle said softly. "You've hardly said two words all evening. Do I make you feel uncomfortable?"

"No." She lied without remorse, steeling herself to return his gaze. Damn him! she thought viciously. He knew very well how ill-at-ease he was making her with his all-seeing look. She felt oddly exposed in spite of the fact that the caftan covered her from her neck to her toes.

"You haven't even asked what decision I've reached regarding Drew and your sister," Kyle pointed out.

"I assumed you'd tell me anything you wanted me to know."

"Most impressive, Corey! You've demonstrated that, unlike most women, you're not given to prying. But aren't you the least bit concerned?"

"I can't honestly say that I am. I'm convinced Jan and Drew are in love, and while I hope things go as smoothly as possible for them, I think that whatever happens they'll manage somehow."

"In other words, the old 'love conquers all' theory."

"I suppose that's a simple way of putting it."

"It's not only simple, it's simplistic!" Kyle said forcefully. "And since Lorraine tells me you've had an un-

happy marriage of your own, I'm surprised to hear you
still believe in that hokum."

"Yes, well, it's just that I don't make the mistake of
thinking my experience is universal. Anyway," she
added, "there was hardly love on my husband's side. If
there had been, things might have turned out to be quite
different."

"How *did* it turn out?" Kyle asked gently.

"It was annulled." Corey shrugged, pretending a de-
tachment she didn't feel. "My stepmother was buying
and Lance was selling."

"And after that you can still delude yourself that he
wouldn't have sold you out if he'd really loved you!"

"Everyone lives by one 'delusion' or another. If that's
what you choose to call it, feel free. But if you refuse
to acknowledge the importance of love, how would you
account for all the successful marriages?"

Now it was Kyle who shrugged. "I'll grant you that
love might help to overcome the problems that are inevitable in married life until passion is spent and the
honeymoon is over. Studies have shown that for the
average couple, that only takes about ten days—which
is an interesting coincidence, since Lorraine says that's
about how long your marriage lasted. But in the long
run, other factors are far more important."

Corey gritted her teeth to keep from crying out at the
awful inaccuracy of his statement, because there hadn't
been much passion in her marriage either—at least, not
on her part. At the time she'd blamed herself for this.
Lance had blamed her, too. He'd said she was cold.
Since then, however, she'd begun to wonder if she
wouldn't have been more responsive if Lance had been
a more considerate lover. Whenever he'd made love to
her, she'd gotten the impression that her presence was
incidental, that, in reality, he was making love to himself.

Now it required every ounce of self-control she possessed to inquire evenly, "Such as?"

"Maturity. Common interests. The attitude of each of
the partners toward the concept of marriage and family.

Last, but surely not least, *money*. Next to those things, love is so much chaff—easily dispersed by the first ill wind."

"I notice you especially emphasize money," Corey observed coolly.

"Why not? More marriages end in divorce because of disagreements over finances than for any other reason. And it's a problem Drew and Jan will have to face from the beginning."

"But it's in your power to help them over that particular hurdle."

"Which was the main thrust of our meeting tonight," Kyle said wryly. "The thing is, I'm not sure that it would be wise for me to help them. Drew's ideas on the subject are positively juvenile. Or, no—they're even worse than that. Most children are more realistic than he is. He spouts a lot of garbage full of 'isms.' According to him, anything that hints of a profit motive is separatist, sexist, racist, fascist, atheist—well, you name it. But the truth of the matter is, he never quite recovered from the disillusionment of learning that a nickel isn't worth two dimes even if it is twice as big. Ever since then, in his view, money is of no importance whatsoever."

"Is that so surprising?" Corey asked. "Isn't that merely the reverse of your belief that it's *all* important?"

"Did I say that?" he shot back at her.

If Corey had thought her question might dent his armor of cock-sureness, she was mistaken. Now the tables were turned and it was she who was on the defensive. Her heart was hammering almost painfully beneath her breastbone. Why were Lorraine and Nate taking so long? she wondered frantically. And why had she ever started to argue with Kyle?

"Did I say that, Corey?" Kyle repeated softly. His narrowed eyes demanded a response.

"No, but you implied—"

"That's a debatable point," he cut in, "but I won't quibble over it. I'll admit I think money is vitally important, never more so than when you don't have any, but it's not by any means my be-all or end-all. What I *do* believe is that everyone, like your ex-husband, has their price. I believe that from strictly selfish motives *anyone* can be brought to the point of doing things that seem alien to his nature. All that's necessary is to give the right incentive. A person may sell out for money, for job advancement, for power, for sex—Hell! There are any number of reasons. But sell out he will."

Why should she feel the sting of tears at the backs of her eyes? Corey asked herself. From what Drew had told her about his brother, she'd known Kyle had been hurt by his father's experience with unscrupulous women. Surely this firsthand evidence of his cynicism hadn't made her feel like crying out of sympathy for him? And if it had, her sympathy would be wasted. He was not the kind of man who would want anyone to cry for him. Uncertain of her voice, she remained silent.

"No comment?" he goaded her. "I'd have expected you to leap to the defense of your romantic philosophy."

Corey cleared her throat. "I disagree with you, of course, but arguments alone won't change your opinion."

"Very astute." Kyle issued the compliment so bitingly, he gave the words the ring of an insult. "Perhaps *you* could, though."

"I don't understand."

"Drew sings your praises, did you know that? He's talked about you more than he has about Jan. I could almost suspect that he's gotten in over his head with her because she's your sister. He believes you're above corruption, and for his own protection he has to be taught that there's no such animal as an incorruptible person. To show you how gullible he is, he even believes you were actually unaware of his family connection with Zachary Electronics until last night."

"But I was," she protested hotly.

"Next thing you'll claim is that you didn't know that Jan and Drew have been using your apartment as their love nest."

Under Kyle's dispassionate gaze, the color drained

from Corey's face and she could only shake her head in denial.

"All of the evidence indicates you knew they were meeting at your place," he said crisply. "You gave Jan her own key. You knew they'd become more than friends. You're not so naive that you're ignorant of the likelihood that a young couple who are spending as much time together as Jan and Drew have been are also sleeping with each other." Kyle laughed mirthlessly. "Even Lorraine knew they were using your apartment. Lorraine may be your best friend, but she admits she can't understand how you could have remained blind to the situation for very long. After all, there are certain tell-tale signs—"

"I don't have to defend myself to you," Corey interrupted sharply.

He'd pushed her too far, and all at once she was blazingly angry—at Kyle for his cynical condemnation, at Lorraine for coercing her into this night, at herself for having been intimidated by Kyle. Her anger rescued her from passive acceptance, and she sprang to her feet and stalked angrily to the door. She'd already opened it when Kyle spoke again.

"Bravo, Corey!" he applauded ironically. "You've reminded me of the danger of jumping to conclusions. Here I thought you'd *welcome* an opportunity to help your sister."

For an instant she remained motionless in the doorway, then she slowly turned to face him. Even as she did so she knew that she was being lured into a trap, but she was foolishly unable to resist the bait.

"What do you mean by that?" she asked.

"For all his gibes about how self-indulgent people are, Drew is too addicted to the good life to give it up so easily. When push comes to shove, if I don't agree to continue his allowance, he'll never go through with the marriage."

Kyle stopped her protests with an impatient wave of his hand.

"I know you don't agree," he acknowledged, "but that's beside the point. What's important to you, especially since Jan is pregnant, is to see her safely married, her baby's future secure. Is that a fair statement?"

Corey nodded jerkily. "I should think you'd want the same thing," she said. "After all, it's your own niece or nephew whose well-being is at stake as well as Jan's."

Kyle's mouth thinned to a hard line. "It's a wise child who knows his own father," he quoted tonelessly, "but whether it's Drew's child is irrelevant, too. The crux of the matter is that it's within your hands to guarantee that I'll underwrite the marriage until Drew has his degree."

The flame of her anger was fanned even higher by his careless indictment of her sister, and she curled her hands into fists and glowered at him while a hot tide of furious color washed into her face.

"Jan and Drew have agreed to spend the next week at our cottage at Lake Geneva," Kyle said. "In fact, they're driving down there tonight after Drew's gig. Our sister, Maureen, and her husband, Mitch Saunders, and their children will be there. Ostensibly it will give us all a chance to get to know Jan a little better and vice versa.

"All you have to do is come along. If you can make it through the week without giving in to whatever temptations I can manage to place in your path—without selling out on your principles—I'll continue Drew's allowance. My only other condition is that you keep this arrangement confidential."

"B-but you know n-nothing about me," she stammered. "How will you know whether or not—"

"Believe me, Corey," he assured her with frightening authority, "I'll be the first to know."

"You said everyone has a price. If I go along with you, won't that constitute *my* price? I'd be beaten before I started."

"I can see you'll be a worthy adversary, but I promise you there are no word tricks involved here. If you'll recall, I said that a sell-out had to be for selfish reasons." He grinned roguishly. He was enjoying watching her try to wriggle out of the snare he'd set. "If you agree to do this, would it be an act of selfishness on your part?"

"Yes," she retorted caustically, "because I'd relish being the one to make you eat your words!"

Kyle's laughter rang out, shattering the charged atmosphere between them, leaving her bewildered. Lazily, he got to his feet and walked toward her. He covered the width of the room with a few long, pantherlike strides and stopped directly in front of her—so near she could feel the heat of his body. Raising one hand from his side, he touched a lock of her hair and lifted it from her shoulder. He tested its silkiness and twined it absently between his fingers before he grasped a handful of hair near the nape of her neck and pulled at it gently, forcing her to tilt her head back.

His face was so close to hers that she could taste the fruity warmth of the wine on his breath, so close she could focus clearly on only one feature. She settled on his eyes, heavy-lidded and gleaming darkly, shadowed by a fringe of short thick lashes. The expression she read in them was so intimate that she felt giddy and hurriedly closed her own eyes.

He ran the backs of his fingers along the line of her jaw until his hand cradled the base of her skull beneath the shining curtain of her hair. With his thumb he lightly traced the outline of her lips, and suddenly she was trembling. What was worse was that she knew Kyle was aware of the intensity of her reaction to him.

"If you win, I'll admit I'm wrong," he promised softly. "That'll be a bonus for you."

"And if you win?" she whispered.

"When I win, Corey," he corrected her, *warned* her. "When I win, *you'll* be my bonus."

Later that night in her darkened bedroom, Corey acknowledged that the battle lines were drawn. She only wished they'd been more clearly defined. She'd tried to argue with Kyle, to reason with him. She'd pointed out

that she had a job and could hardly be expected to take
time off without prior notice.

"That's your problem, not mine" had been his callous
response.

"How can you say that when you're making your
brother's financial welfare dependent on me?" she asked.

With an indifferent shrug, Kyle had replied, "You can
always refuse."

After all was said and done, of course, she hadn't
refused. That she would take up the gauntlet he'd thrown
down had been a foregone conclusion. If her marriage
had accomplished no other purpose, it had taught her that
it was useless to try to run away from a problem. She
might feel animosity for Kyle, yet all he'd had to do was
touch her face and her bones had turned to jelly. The
best way to deal with the undeniable physical attraction
she felt for him was to face up to it and hope that it
would fade with propinquity.

By the time she had given up sparring with Kyle and
returned to her apartment, it was after midnight. In spite
of the fact that she was tired, mentally she was so keyed
up that she'd known she'd never be able to fall asleep
until her emotional turmoil had abated.

What exactly did Kyle have in mind for her? She still
wasn't clear on that, despite her frustrated attempts at
clarification. He meant to buy her off in some unspecified
way, at which point he would *own* her. It was too bizarre
to be believed, yet she shivered with foreboding. She
felt as if she'd made a covenant with the devil himself.

With a sigh, Corey punched her pillow and turned it
over to the cooler surface on the underside. It didn't help
matters that it was still so hot. She never slept well
without the windows open, so she'd turned off the air
conditioner before going to bed. She lay back against the
pillow, only slightly more comfortable.

Surely by reacting so fearfully to Kyle she was at-
tributing more power to him than was humanly possible.
It could even be that, contrary to his stated purpose of

teaching Drew a lesson, Kyle hoped she would prove he
was wrong in his belief that everyone had a price. Let
him trot out his arsenal of weapons and try them on her;
he'd see how ineffective they were.

Mentally she ticked off the possibilities he'd mentioned. Money, job advancement, power. What could he
hope to offer her in those areas as sufficient inducement
to betray her ideals? Absolutely nothing.

And sex. She considered this final avenue of attack
reluctantly. Kyle was well aware of the devastating impact he had on women—on her. She knew intuitively
that this was the quarter she must guard most diligently.
But even if he succeeded in seducing her in the short
space of one week, would she have compromised herself?

Corey bolted to a sitting position on the bed, drawing
her knees to her chin. Then she tucked her body into a
protective ball and pressed her face roughly into the sheet
covering her knees.

God, yes! The answer resounded through her mind.
Because the only way she'd go to bed with Kyle was if
she'd fallen in love with him, and to love a man like
Kyle Zachary would be the ultimate betrayal of her most
fundamental beliefs. After Lance had left her, she'd
vowed that never again would she lead with her heart.

But selfish? Again the answer came unbidden. Of
course it would be selfish.

People often did selfish things under the guise of love.
Look at her father. He'd told himself he was ignoring
her to ease the strife between herself and Vera, but even
when she was a child she hadn't swallowed that! As
she'd grown up, she'd known he'd taken the easy way
out so he wouldn't be subjected to Vera's ugly moods.
He'd never once interfered when Corey had had to endure
her stepmother's verbal abuse. He'd simply tuned all the
unpleasantness out. Nor had he done Vera any favors by
tolerating such awful behavior. In the end, Vera had
alienated everyone she cared about, including her own
daughter. If Tom Kenyon had been truly concerned for

Vera, he'd have helped her to deal constructively with her obsessive jealousy.

"Kyle uses women and throws them away," Drew had said. And "They stand in line for the privilege of being next."

If she were to fall in love with Kyle, if she then yielded to the temptation to have an affair with him, it would be an act of self-gratification because he'd never accept her love nor would he return such a tender emotion. Under such one-sided conditions, there could be no giving, only taking.

Corey lifted her face and stared intently into the darkness. She believed she had worked out what form Kyle's attempts to undermine her integrity would take, but she found little satisfaction in finding this answer. With someone less formidable, her natural inclination would be to remind herself it was only for a week and "forewarned is forearmed," but with Kyle that could only result in dangerous overconfidence. He'd probably intended all along that she should figure out his game plan. Just the thought that she might become the subject of his sensual persuasiveness made her even more aware of him than before.

She recalled the strong lines of his face, his lean loose-limbed body, the predatory grace of his walk. Everything about him hinted at the perils of someone with her limited experience trying to tame his unleashed passions.

For an instant she indulged in the memory of his knowing smile, of the expression of easy intimacy that smoldered in the dark depths of his eyes. Brief as it was, the recollection caused a warmth and languor to invade her limbs and evoked a trembling ache at the pit of her stomach.

With a groan, Corey buried her flushed face in her hands, rubbing her palms in a circular motion over her eyelids to erase the vivid image of Kyle's face. Her victory in having determined his strategy seemed a hollow one at best, and she prayed she hadn't won this initial skirmish only to lose the war.

CHAPTER
Four

BY THE TIME Kyle called for her the next morning, Corey had shaken off her black mood of apprehension and her usual optimism had reasserted itself.

It helped that thunderstorms had rolled through the region just before sunrise, scouring the humidity from the air. The morning dawned crisp and golden, promising a warm, perfect summer's day.

Her horoscope said the time was especially promising for vacations and travel, and that either contracts or romantic liaisons entered into on this date would come to the desired conclusions.

Once Corey had decided that the part about romance had to refer to Jan's wedding, she thought the overall forecast was good. It didn't occur to her that she was acting out of character by attaching so much significance to her horoscope.

It helped that Kyle's manner with her was less intense, almost friendly, and, at the outset, completely without suggestive overtones.

Was he merely trying to lull her into complacency? Corey didn't know, but as they drove southeastward from Madison her fears of the night before seemed groundless; fanciful in the extreme.

When they'd begun their trip, Kyle had surprised her by asking, "Were you able to arrange for time off from your job?"

When she replied that she'd phoned the senior partner of the law firm to ask for vacation time the following week so that she might deal with a "family emergency," and that Mr. Barnes had generously granted her request, he'd smiled and nodded.

"I thought as much," he'd remarked smoothly. "And may I compliment you on your innovative use of the truth." His open smile had removed any hint of sarcasm from the comment.

It also helped that Lorraine had come over just as Corey was finishing her packing and they'd made their peace with one another.

"I'm sorry I was so bitchy last night," Lorraine said as she stood hesitantly in the doorway to the bedroom, her hands clutched in apparent nervousness behind her back. "I don't know what came over me."

"Well, I do," Corey had quipped. "He's tall, dark and good-looking and he makes a steam roller look like a child's toy!"

Lorraine's cheeks pinkened with embarrassment. "No hard feelings?"

"Nary a one!"

"Good." Lorraine brought her hands out in front of her to reveal the red and white bikini she held. "Prove it by letting me give you this."

"Oh, Lorraine, I can't—"

"Please take it, Corey," Lorraine pleaded earnestly. "It's one of those things I bought thinking it would encourage me to lose weight, but you know me: I look at a piece of candy or a rich dessert and I add another pound. So although I've had it for over a year, I've never worn it, and unless some miracle happens, I never will."

Corey watched uncertainly as Lorraine unfolded the tiny scraps of material that comprised the bathing suit and put them on the bed.

"But Lorraine, it's so—so—"

"Nonsense! It's what everyone is wearing. You'll be smashing in it. God, I envy you being able to eat whatever you want without having to worry about gaining an ounce. That's my idea of heaven."

Finally, afraid of hurting her friend's feelings if she refused the gift, Corey accepted it, promising Lorraine she would wear it at the first opportunity.

After Lorraine had said good-bye, she'd hurried to finish folding her clothes into her suitcases. She hadn't a large wardrobe, and out of necessity the things she owned were inexpensive, but she had an eye for style and for coordinating accessories. And although she wasn't very tall, she had a long-legged, fine-boned build that gave whatever she wore a flair that was distinctly her own. Because she disliked calling attention to herself, most of her things, like the natural-colored linen-look slacks and silky café-au-lait blouse she was wearing, were in quiet colors. She would never have chosen such a minuscule bikini for herself, much less a *red* one piped with white but, recalling her promise to Lorraine, at the last minute she tucked it into her bag. At least it took up no space.

Kyle arrived soon afterward, bearing a luxuriant Boston fern as a hostess gift for an ecstatic Lorraine, who was agog all over again at the sight of him. Corey had to admit he was something to see in the close-fitting brushed denim slacks he wore with a darker blue open-collared shirt. Lorraine trailed after him into Corey's living room, gushing about how sweet he was to have remembered that she was in mourning for a similar plant that had recently died.

Sweet? Corey silently scoffed, as Lorraine's thank yous went on and on. She could think of lots of words to describe Kyle, but sweet certainly wasn't one of them!

As he'd scooped up her luggage, Kyle had caught her eye and informed her, "I have the top down on the car."

Without waiting for a response, still shadowed by Lorraine, he'd gone on ahead of her to load her suitcases in the back of a sleek Mercedes sports car. "My sister's car," he'd explained curtly when Lorraine began raving about it.

Corey had pulled her hair back and tucked it under a perky visor-cap to keep it from blowing. "If he was sweet," she muttered, "he'd have asked if I prefer the top down or up!" But then she'd scolded herself for grumbling. If he'd asked her, she'd have chosen to leave it down, too.

As they wound their way through the city, Corey caught Kyle studying her whenever they were stopped at a traffic light. Finally, rightly assuming that her heightened color was a result of the fact that he'd been staring at her, Kyle said, "I don't mean to embarrass you. It's just that you're so different now from the way you looked last night." He grinned and the effect was devastating to her pulse rate. "You're hardly a femme fatale, are you? Today you look all of fifteen, and not even, by any stretch of the imagination, a very precocious fifteen."

"It's difficult to get heart and soul into the siren image in broad daylight," she retorted peevishly. "Especially when one is handicapped by an open car."

"I guess I put my foot in it with that remark. Unlike most women, you apparently don't take it as a compliment when you're told you look much younger than you are."

"If you'd ever been passed over for promotion because of a thing like that, you'd know why I don't! People usually tend to assume that looking young is a sign of general immaturity, and I get angry when I'm called on to prove that I'm a responsible adult simply due to physical characteristics over which I have no control. Other people don't have to put up with that, so why should I?"

"What would you like to be told instead? That you have a beautiful body and gorgeous legs?"

She met his eyes levelly, not wanting to give him the satisfaction of knowing how much he had unnerved her. "That would be an improvement at least, but what I'd really prefer is that people made no comments at all regarding my appearance."

"Shall we make polite small talk about the weather then," Kyle suggested smoothly, "and tell each other things we can see for ourselves about how nice it's been since the storm ended?"

"Silence is golden," she snapped. "Why don't we try a little of that."

Her attitude mellowed, however, as they traveled through the gently undulating green of the countryside. The slopes were patterned with contour plowed croplands interspersed with windrows or woodlots that made a lovely, irregular checkerboard design on the landscape. Here and there, clusters of farm buildings added accents of barn red and silo blue to the overall verdancy of the scene. The sky was sunny and cloudless, and the wind warm and soft against her cheek. It was too marvelous a day to be a grouch or bear a grudge.

"You really *don't* talk very much, do you?" Kyle asked, breaking the curiously companionable silence between them.

"Not unless I have something to say," she agreed sweetly. "Is there something you'd like to discuss?"

"You could tell me what's growing in these fields."

"Tobacco," she replied tersely, relenting somewhat to add, "The barns with the funny slatted sides are for curing the crops."

Another silence followed.

"You could explain why you keep craning your neck and peering at passing cars so strangely. Are you a back-seat driver?"

"I'm reading the license plates."

"I've heard of compulsive readers, but that's a new one on me."

"There are so many personalized ones. I think you'd be surprised what revealing information people put on them. You can discover their hobbies, their philosophies of life, the way they regard their cars—all kinds of things."

"I imagine mostly you find out how corny people can be in six letters or less!"

"Not al all," she said stiffly. A lot of them are clever."

"For instance?"

"Well—two of the most creative ones I've seen are 10SNE1 and META4."

"What's that first one? 10-SNE-1 . . . I don't get it."

Corey chuckled. "See what I mean about cleverness? It's 'Tennis, anyone?'" She laughed again, then continued. "A gracious one I saw the other day was T 4 2. And don't you think people with DO IT and GO4IT are determined types?"

He nodded and smiled, clearly showing her he was enjoying her observation on license plates and wanted her to go on.

"The friendliest is a tossup between HI YALL and HOWDY. The most apt was in a wedding party. The plates on the car the bride and groom were in read CLOUD9."

"Not bad." He grinned.

"My dentist's license is TUTH DR."

"Is that why you go to him?"

"Certainly," she said, laughing at the foolishness of both question and answer.

"Would you order personalized plates for your own car?"

"No."

"I rest my case."

"But only because I can't think of anything really original to put on them."

"Interesting," he commented facetiously. "Tell me, Corey, what do you read besides license plates?"

"Oh, lots of things. Graffiti, bumper stickers, cereal boxes, billboards. . . . I've often regretted the demise of the old Burma Shave signs because I'm especially fond of limericks."

"Books?" he inquired.

"Not if I can help it," she fibbed airily.

"It's just as I thought!" He nodded. "You're an intellectual snob."

"You—you're so damned sure of yourself," she sputtered. "I'll bet you do crossword puzzles in ink!"

She darted a sidelong look at him. For an instant his expression showed that he was startled by the accuracy of her insight. It made him seem more approachable somehow, and Corey found her irritation dissolving in amusement.

Because he was driving into the glare of the morning sun, Kyle was wearing sunglasses. She couldn't see his eyes, but his mouth was quirked up at the corners, his lean cheeks creased by a grin. Her glance took in his dark hair, ruffled by the wind, his sinewy forearm that was propped on the driver's door with his hand cupping the rushing air. Her eyes rested for a time on his angular profile, then skidded to the strong sunbrowned column of his neck.

She quickly looked away, concentrating fixedly on the cornfields and pastures whizzing by. "I really do read all those things I mentioned." Her voice seemed to catch in her throat. "And I actually enjoy most of them, but I read books, too. As you said, I'm a compulsive reader."

Her admission led to a lively discussion in which they discovered they shared a fondness for murder mysteries—the more lurid the better—for the poetry of T.S. Eliot, and for the Tolkien trilogy.

"That's funny," she mused. "I wouldn't have thought you'd enjoy *Lord of the Rings*."

"And I'd have thought you've been too shielded from the seamy side of life to be capable of appreciating *The Wasteland*."

There was an element of harshness in the way Kyle said this. It struck Corey that he resented the link this established between them, tenuous though it was, and that he wished to retreat before their budding friendship could blossom.

Now, how in the world do I know that about him? she asked herself. She caught her lower lip between her teeth as she worried over this question, marveling at the sureness of her conviction.

Kyle was a type of man who in her humdrum existence

was as alien as if he'd come from another planet. In most respects he was a total enigma to her. How strange that she should find this single facet of his behavior so transparent, that she should be able to label it, ascribe a motive to it.

It was not until they had left the small college community of Whitewater behind and were traveling through the glacier-carved terrain of the Kettle Moraine on the final leg of the journey that she arrived at the answer to her question.

Neither of them had spoken again. Kyle seemed to be as deep in contemplation as she was. Suddenly it dawned on Corey that she was *relieved* he'd called a halt to the conversation and that she'd recognized his escape into silence for the defense it was because it was a tactic *she* herself used to keep others at a distance. In her case it had become second nature—a reflex. Why did she get the impression that for Kyle it was a new and disturbing way of handling a person? Corey was still puzzling over this when Kyle turned off the highway onto a narrow private drive that ended at the parking lot of a restaurant on the western shore of Lake Geneva.

"Why are we stopping here?" she asked.

Kyle hooked the sunglasses over the visor and consulted his wristwatch. "I made arrangments earlier in the week to have lunch with some friends here today. I think you'd enjoy meeting them, and I'd like you to join us."

Corey eyed the soaring roof of the wood and glass building doubtfully. The restaurant was built into the side of a bluff, with a terrace extending over the water. The view from the dining room was probably fabulous, but the place looked expensive, and she wasn't dressed for it.

"You look as cool as coffee ice cream and about that good to eat," Kyle commented, grinning because her thoughts had been so obvious. Tilting his head to one side, he studied her more critically. "But why do you torture your hair like that?"

Before she could stop him, he reached out and removed her cap so that her hair tumbled in silky disarray about her shoulders. She sat speechless while he combed his fingers through it to loosen it.

"That's better," he proclaimed when he'd finished.

At last Corey found her voice. "You've got a nerve. I happen to prefer it the other way."

"Why?" he persisted.

"I just do. I don't have to have a reason."

"Leave it down," Kyle argued softly as she began to pull it up and back. "At the risk of torpedoing the development of friendly relations between us by paying you another personal compliment, you look very sweet with your hair down."

"Sweet! What makes you think I want to look sweet? Did you like it when Lorraine described you in such a bland, insipid way?"

"As a favor to me then." Kyle was obviously amused, for his eyes were warm with humor and his lips twitched with suppressed laughter.

Further protests trembled on the tip of her tongue only momentarily before they died. Why make such an issue of it? she asked herself. It was a small enough request that he made.

"All right," she conceded, "since you finally saw your way clear to ask me rather than order me."

As Kyle held the car door open for her, he remarked, "In the future I'll have to remember that you're such a soft touch—in more ways than one!"

"You make me sound like a cream puff!" she said in disgust.

"Is that so terrible? Lots of people like cream puffs."

"For a change of pace maybe, but they're not very sustaining or satisfying as a daily diet."

"Ahhh, I see," he said knowingly. "You'd rather be thought of as something essential to life—bread perhaps."

The conversation was rapidly getting out of hand, and Corey decided to try to put a stop to it.

"I'd rather we just went inside and had lunch. All this

talk of food has made me hungry."

"Me too," Kyle said. "But I'll give you fair warning, Corey Kenyon, I'm not necessarily hungry for lunch."

CHAPTER
Five

THE RESTAURANT TURNED out to be much less formal
than its exterior had led Corey to believe. They went in
through the bar, which was crowded, noisy, and smoky.
Kyle took her hand to prevent them from being separated
as he shouldered a pathway through the milling people.

They walked down a long hallway and passed through
heavy, iron-studded doors that deadened the noise from
the bar. Further on was the dining room, spacious and
cool and dimly lighted. Its decor featured dark leather
and bright textiles, rough-plastered walls and massive
open beams. A marimba band was playing a haunting
version of *Spanish Eyes* as they threaded their way
through the tables.

She was impressed by the number of friendly greetings
that were called out to Kyle. He seemed to know everyone in the room. One man rose, swaying drunkenly,
when they passed his table. He pumped Kyle's hand and
clapped him heartily on the back.

"Kyle, old buddy, good to see you!" His bleary-eyed
glance took in Corey. "Well, well! New talent, eh?" He
nudged Kyle in the ribs with his elbow and leered at her.
"Where's Gillian today?"

"She had to make a trip to Chicago."

"Deserted you, has she?" The man seemed to find this
possibility very funny.

"She'll be back tomorrow," Kyle said, propelling Corey ahead of him with one hand on her shoulder as he left the man behind.

She felt oddly deflated by the information that Gillian, whoever *she* might be, was out of town and therefore unavailable to Kyle for the time being. Would he have brought her along to have lunch with his friends if Gillian hadn't been in Chicago? Definitely not, she concluded with painful honesty, though why it should be painful she couldn't say. After all, what was Kyle Zachary to her?

They reached their table without further interruption. It was near the windows overlooking the lake, but Corey had time only for a glimpse of the breathtaking view. The booth Kyle led her to was already occupied by a pleasant-appearing, sandy-haired couple who smiled a friendly welcome at her. As they approached, the man got to this feet.

"Corey Kenyon," Kyle introduced them, "these are my friends Tony DiLoretto and his wife, Jill. They're two of our most talented local artists."

"Nice to meet you, Corey," Tony beamed at her while his wife nodded agreement.

Kyle stood to one side, inviting Corey to slide into the banquette. As she seated herself beside Jill, a sloe-eyed cocktail waitress in a frilly, low-cut peasant dress delivered a round of drinks to their table. Tony must have ordered in anticipation of their arrival, because she placed a margarita in front of each of them.

Kyle's eyes intercepted hers over the rim of his glass. "Down the hatch," he toasted. "It's good for what ails you."

Her eyes shied away from his. How could he possibly know what ailed her when even she didn't? she wondered irritably. She sensed he was still watching her, so she raised her glass to her lips and was surprised to find the frothy, lime-flavored drink tasted good after the long drive.

As if he had lost interest in her now that she had

complied with his wishes, Kyle turned away, leaning across the table to start a conversation with Tony about an exhibition that was being planned at an art gallery in Williams Bay.

After taking another sip of her drink, Corey smiled at Jill.

"I noticed you met Carl Lindstrom on your way in," Jill said.

"Do you mean the man who spoke to Kyle?"

Jill nodded.

Corey felt vaguely uneasy. "I wasn't actually introduced. He only made a few comments to Kyle about someone named Gillian."

"I hope Carl didn't make too big an ass of himself. Before Gillian got her hooks into him, he was one of the nicest guys around. She jilted him, you know, literally at the altar."

"No," Corey said. "I didn't know."

"You must not live around here," Jill said in a dry voice.

Corey shook her head. "I'm from Madison."

"Well, that explains it then. Gillian led Carl such a chase that almost everyone around here knew what was going on. During their engagement, there were even pools—sort of like football pools—and people were laying bets as to how long they'd stay together."

"But that's awful!" Corey wrinkled her nose. "It's so—so ghoulish."

"I know," Jill agreed. "I got stuck with a really lousy number myself, so I was just as glad the wedding never came off."

Corey laughed, enjoying the older woman's gossipy frankness.

"Carl and Gillian were childhood sweethearts and he followed after her like a puppy dog all through high school. Once she went away to college, she never showed any real interest in him until he had a fling with another girl. Let me tell you, she broke that up in a hurry. I suppose she was accustomed to him always being at her beck and call, but after she'd won him back, she didn't want him any more." Pulling a long face, Jill concluded, "Unlike Kyle, Carl just can't cope with Gillian."

A rather tense silence followed that was ended when both women began to speak at once.

"You go first," Jill said wryly. "I don't seem to have it in me to find an easy topic of conversation just now. Believe me, Corey, I'm not usually so dense that I discuss a possible rival with a man's date."

They smiled at one another, each of them appreciating Jill's forthrightness, and the ice was broken between them.

"I was only going to ask what kind of artwork you do," said Corey.

"I'm really only a weekend artist," Jill explained, "a dabbler in photography. We have a baby who keeps me too busy to allow me much free time during the week, so I work only on Saturdays and Sundays and the odd afternoon in midweek when a high school girl can look after Dana for me."

"Do you specialize in a certain kind of photography?"

"I do portraits mostly—character studies. Lately I've been experimenting with different combinations of film, filters, exposure times, and processing to get the effect I'm after. I'm not sure just how to explain it." Jill hesitated briefly. "Have you ever seen a daguerreotype or an old sepia-tone photograph?"

Corey nodded, her interest obvious.

"Well, that's more or less the impression I'd like to achieve in my work. Not in color, but in overall mood. I'd like to develop that nostalgic, timeless look that somehow suggests the subject is the idealized example of a given type of person."

"How do you decide which type your subjects should represent?"

Jill laughed. "Now we've arrived at the kernel of the problem, because that can either be very easy or very hard. Sometimes it just leaps out at me. Take Kyle, for instance," she said in a low tone, nodding toward him.

"He's the perfect model of the swashbuckling hero type."
Leaning closer to Corey, she whispered, "God, but he's
outrageously sexy! If I ever decide to lust after any man
but Tony, it will definitely have to be Kyle."

"I see what you mean," Corey murmured, allowing
her eyes to dwell for a few heart-stopping moments on
Kyle's rugged profile. With his compelling combination
of physical attractiveness and raw animal magnetism, the
problem was how *not* to lust after him.

"Now, tell me," Jill said briskly, forcing Corey to tear
her eyes away from Kyle, "what's the first thing that
strikes you about Tony?"

Corey looked at Jill's husband, noting his light-brown
hair and neatly trimmed beard, the wholesomeness of his
blunt-featured face, the intelligence showing in his hazel
eyes that twinkled good-naturedly behind metal-rimmed
glasses.

"The first thing I notice is how much the two of you
resemble each other, but I'm sure that's not what you're
after."

"No, but it's interesting all the same how often a
married couple will look enough alike to be brother and
sister. No doubt it shows a healthy dose of egotism to
choose a mate so much like oneself."

Under Jill's expectant gaze, Corey tried again. "After
that, there are two things about Tony that stand out. He
looks like an intellectual, but the size of his hands and
the muscles in his forearms seem to indicate that he's a
man who does manual labor."

"Hey, that's very good! Tony's looks illustrate that
he's exactly what he is—a damned good sculptor!"

Leaning back against the bench, Jill scanned the room
and pointed out the girl who had served their drinks.
"Do you see our waitress over there? Everything about
her virtually shrieks *Lolita!* Can't you just see her as a
lovely little nymphet?"

Captivated by this play of imagination, Corey smiled
and nodded. "What about the difficult ones?" she asked.

"Fortunately they're fairly rare because I'm so in-

volved with faces, but even so, certain people elude me.
You, for example. I think it might be very hard to confine
you to a single image." After studying Corey's face,
feature by feature, Jill ventured, "Maybe it's your eyes.
There's a kind of hungry expression there that might be
impossible to capture in a still photo, but whatever the
reason, you could be anything—saint or sinner or anyone
in between. I wonder why?"

Corey was uncomfortably aware that the men had
ended their conversation and were listening intently to
Jill and her. Smiling faintly, she said, "Perhaps it's because I'm still undecided!"

"That's an interesting notion," Tony inserted. "It im-
plies that you have faith that one has the freedom to
choose, and that we aren't cast into an unbreakable mold
by predestination, genes, gut reactions, or de ol' debbil
glands!"

"Oh, there's no question but that each of those things
limits our alternatives to some extent," Corey returned
pensively. "But people must have faith that there are
some options open to them. Otherwise what's the purpose
of living?"

"Are you aware that much of the world's populace
would disagree with you?" Tony countered.

"That doesn't mean they're right and I'm wrong."

"I can see you have the courage of your convictions,"
said Jill. Turning to Kyle, she asked, "What do you
believe? Do we or do we not have any freedom of choice
as to our eventual destiny?"

"Well, I don't know for sure, so like most people I've
tried to tag all the bases," Kyle rejoined with tongue-in-
cheek humor. "When faced with a tough decision, I've
read the Bible, the Koran, Confucius, and the Torah.
I've consulted gypsy fortune tellers, tea leaves, and on
occasion a Ouija board or fortune cookies. The result is
that most of the time I've plunged right ahead and done
whatever it was that I wanted to do in the first place,
since one of those sources is certain to offer justification
for almost any action."

They all laughed, and an easy give-and-take was established between the four of them as their meal was served. The lunch was a leisurely one, and by the time they'd finished, Corey felt as if the DiLorettos were old friends. When Kyle announced that his sister was expecting them and it was past time they should be leaving, Jill bade Corey a fond good-bye and Tony kissed her cheek soundly and whispered, "You're much nicer than Gillian."

Before Corey could stop herself, she had muttered, "From what Jill's told me about her, that's not saying very much," but Tony only laughed and hugged her.

"I'll try to do better next time," he promised as he released her, speaking loudly enough that Kyle overheard him.

"What was that all about?" Kyle asked curtly when they were walking across the parking lot. "It looked to me as if Tony did quite well enough for himself."

Corey shook her head silently and was thankful when Kyle didn't press her for an explanation. Neither of them spoke again until they were in the Mercedes, heading toward the highway.

Wanting to break the oppressive silence, Corey hesitantly said, "Th-thank you for taking me to lunch. I liked your friends."

"One of them especially," Kyle said.

"Yes," she conceded coolly. "Jill and I got along very well."

Kyle expressed his skepticism with a derisive hoot.

It was a relief for Corey to be at loggerheads with him again. She felt she could cope with that state of affairs far better than with his dangerous attraction.

"Are we back to square one?" she asked tartly. "Have you decided now that I get my jollies breaking up happy homes?"

"I don't know," Kyle said flatly.

He swerved the car over to the side of the drive, switched the engine off, and turned to face her.

"As Jill said, you could be either a saint or a sinner.

Suppose we find out which one you are."

His hands grasped her shoulders and pulled her roughly toward him. She opened her mouth to object and recognized her crucial tactical blunder when his mouth covered hers. If he'd continued with his rough handling of her, she would have persisted in her attempt to protest, she would have fought him somehow, but his kiss was gently persuasive, coaxing her response rather than demanding it, until her lips willingly softened for him.

Assured of her capitulation, his kiss assumed a greater urgency and the pressure of his mouth on hers increased, forcing her lips farther apart. As his tongue teased, tasted, probed deep and yet deeper, exploring the sweet recesses of her mouth, Corey was buffeted by a hot, soul-destroying wave of desire. She felt she would drown in its wake and she clung to Kyle, clutching weakly at his shoulders.

She became aware that he'd freed the buttons of her blouse only when his hands coasted silkily over her rib cage finally to capture her breasts. With his thumbs he delicately outlined the nipples until they eagerly rose to meet his touch through the lacy material of her bra. Each separate nerve ending in her body seemed to vibrate in response to the least caress of his knowing fingertips, and she was seized by uncontrollable trembling.

She was so lost in these new sensations that it no longer mattered that she was merely a stand-in for Gillian. It no longer mattered that Kyle had misjudged and insulted her. She even forgot about their bargain, and it wasn't until much later that it dawned on her that Kyle must have forgotten about it too.

At that moment, all that seemed to matter was that Kyle should go on kissing her, holding her, touching her. She had never experienced such a mindless, glorious, primitive need, and it seemed so miraculous to her that she desperately wanted him to lead her on to its natural conclusion.

When Kyle tore his mouth away from hers, she turned her face toward his, blindly seeking his lips, instinctively trying to prolong contact with him until he withdrew his hands from her breasts and put her firmly away from him.

"Button your blouse," he ordered harshly.

She flinched as if he'd struck her and almost whimpered at her deprivation.

Kyle's face was closed and coldly aloof. His hands lay relaxed and open on the steering wheel and were completely steady while hers were shaking so badly she could hardly follow his instructions. Her breath came in ragged gasps and the blood was rushing through her ears, throbbing almost painfully in her temples.

At last, muttering an oath beneath his breath, he pushed her hands aside and efficiently completed the task himself.

Numb with shock, Corey fixed her eyes on his hands. When he had finished, she shoved her own hands into the pockets of her slacks to hide their trembling and made herself as small as possible on the passenger side of the car.

"You're a regular little bundle of contradictions, aren't you, Corey?" Kyle exclaimed mockingly. "You may not talk very much, but when you want to, you can be incredibly quick with words. Yet now you choose to remain so damnably silent. Don't you want to know what fascinating things I learned about you with my experiment?"

"Whether or not I want to know is immaterial, since you're undoubtedly going to tell me anyway," she replied bitterly.

"Yes, I am," he agreed levelly. "I learned that by some miracle that's beyond my comprehension, you're an innocent—"

"You're forgetting I've been married."

"I said innocent, not virgin. And there is a difference, Corey. My guess is that you're relatively inexperienced. Most women are *born* knowing more about men than you seem to."

Kyle paused as if giving her a chance to confirm or deny his surmise, but his use of the word "experiment" to describe what to her had been an earth-shaking encounter had had the effect of a lighted match touched to the flashpoint of her temper, and she stared stonily straight ahead through the windshield.

"So you're an innocent," Kyle repeated, "albeit a very dissatisfied one. You'd like to be a 'sinner' and you're looking for some poor devil to show you the way. Well, lady," he advised her savagely, "you got a wrong number with me!"

"How dare you!" she gasped, turning to glare at him indignantly. "You're the one who put the moves on me, yet you act as if I'd tried to seduce *you!*"

"Didn't you? Corey, be honest with yourself." He shook his head slightly. "I know a come-on when I see it, and I'd have to be blind not to recognize the one you've been giving me all afternoon."

"What have you got against innocents, anyway?" she mumbled.

"Oh, Corey—" was all Kyle managed to say before his disapproval dissolved in laughter that rumbled out from deep in his chest.

Nervously at first, she joined in until she, too, was laughing with real amusement. They laughed so hard that tears ran down their cheeks and they fell weakly into one another's arms for mutual support. But at some point, Corey passed over the edge of humor. Her hard-won control snapped and tears came as a result of the sobs that shook her.

Kyle held her, murmuring sympathetically and stroking her back, until the storm of weeping had passed. Finally she began to regain her composure, and while she was mopping at her swollen eyes with his handkerchief, he apologized.

"I guess I was pretty rough on you," he said gruffly, "but it was for your own good, Corey. There are any number of men who'd have taken advantage of your willingness without a qualm."

"How lucky for me you're so high minded!" Her ironic tone of voice was partially muffled by the handkerchief, and she decided that was for the better. Not for the world would she reveal to Kyle that, except for Lance, she'd withheld herself from the men who made passes at her. Until him.

"It's not a matter of being high minded," he corrected her stiffly, "and it's nothing against you personally. What it amounts to is self-preservation. Women like you play for keeps. They tend to expect marriage in return for the dubious honor of sleeping with them, and I'm not ready to put my neck in that noose."

"I see your point." Affecting frivolity, she confronted him with an obviously bogus pout. "But if all men ascribed to that bias, how would a poor, underprivileged, underachiever like me ever get any experience?"

When she saw that Kyle was staring at her in stunned disbelief, as if his ears must be deceiving him, she added for good measure, "Not only that, I'll bet the human race would soon be faced with extinction!"

"My God, Corey! Do you know you are the most maddening, incorrigible—"

"I'm not sure." She waggled her eyebrows at him and flicked ash from an imaginary cigar. "Hum a few bars and I'll tell you."

Groaning with laughter, Kyle buried his head in his hands. "That's the worst Groucho Marx impression I've ever seen or heard!" he exclaimed. "You may not have what it takes to be a saint, but you'd certainly try the patience of one."

CHAPTER
Six

"PREPARE TO COME ABOUT." The order was smartly given.

"Aye-aye, captain." With a jaunty salute, Corey complied, shifting her body weight from starboard to port as Greg Saunders brought the bow of the sloop through the eye of the wind, then setting the jib sail for the new tack.

"See how the jib is luffing. You're letting it spill too much wind," Gregg instructed. "Try trimming it just until it stops fluttering and you feel a little resistance on the sheet and see what happens."

She gave the jib sheet another wrap around the cleat and the responsive little boat heeled a bit more sharply and gained way until it seemed they were flying over the sun-sparkled surface of the lake.

Corey laughed exultantly and turned her glowing, spray-dampened face toward Greg. "How's that?"

"Better" was the succinct reply. He cast a critical eye over the smooth swell of the sail before his sober young face split in an approving smile. "You're not doing badly at all, Corey."

She was honored at having earned the compliment. Greg Saunders might be only thirteen, but he took his sailing seriously and he was an exacting instructor. The

61

number of trophies he'd already won attested to his skill and dedication.

His long-range goal was to qualify for the Olympic sailing team, and this year his plan was to become the youngest skipper ever to win the local yacht club's coveted Challenge Cup in his class of boat. This was a tall order considering that there were national and international champions in the fleet. But at the breakfast table that morning, he'd announced glumly, "Chris Hayes had to go to his grandmother's for the week, so he can't crew for me in the Fourth of July races this Friday. Looks like I won't be able to enter."

Only four of them lingered around the table in the sunny alcove by the leaded-glass bay windows of the breakfast nook—Maureen and Mitchel Saunders, Greg, and Corey.

"Surely you can find someone else," Maureen said, clearly sympathetic to her son.

"Everyone who's any good is already spoken for and my other friends aren't interested." The last was said in scathing tones as Greg shook his head in disgust, unable to understand anybody not being interested in sailing.

"What about your sister?" Maureen suggested.

"Oh, Mother!" Greg rolled his eyes toward the ceiling in exasperation. "Betsy's only seven, for cripes sake, and she has an attention span of about ten seconds."

"How about Corey, then?" Mitch Saunders spoke up. "You don't have an age limit since you haven't entered the junior competition and she's not very big."

Greg automatically drew in his breath to give a negative response before he looked toward Corey and paused. His brows came together in a thoughtful frown. Corey probably didn't weigh as much as Chris's one hundred ten pounds and weight was an important factor in the selection of a racing crew.

"Have you ever done any sailing?" he asked her.

"No," she replied amiably, "but I'd like to learn how to handle a sailboat."

"Hmmm—" Greg observed her solemnly, as if measuring her slight form, weighing her sincerity.

Corey eyed him, too. She was pretty sure he was
worried that she wouldn't want to take orders from a
mere kid.

"Maybe you could teach her enough to qualify for the
finals, son," Mitch argued. "That way you'd at least stay
in contention for the cup."

"Hmmm—" Greg repeated before explaining that he
didn't find the idea of finishing low in the standings for
the week's series of races very attractive, but he liked
even less the idea of dropping out of the running for the
trophy. "I suppose it wouldn't hurt to take Corey out and
give her a trial," he finally said grudgingly.

"Greg!" Maureen reprimanded him, smiling apologetically at Corey. "Where are your manners!"

"Sorry," he mumbled around a bite of toast, an embarrassed flush staining his thin young face. "Would you
come out with me, Corey? Even if you don't learn enough
so we can enter the regatta, I could still teach you to
sail."

"Thank you, Greg," she'd agreed gamely. "I'd like
that."

Now it was late afternoon and they were just finishing
her first lesson, tacking on a zigzag course that would
eventually bring them back to the dock in front of the
Zachary summer home. At first they'd ghosted through
gentle little puffs of air that constantly shifted direction
and provided a difficult test for a novice, but Corey had
done well. Then the breeze had gusted more strongly,
though still from unpredictable quarters. Finally the wind
had blown steadily over the port bow, humming through
the rigging. The slender little craft skimmed along hardly
seeming to touch the blue-green water.

It was the second day of her stay at Lake Geneva and
so far it had been quite pleasant. Maureen and Mitch
were easy to like. In their middle thirties, the couple was
extremely attractive. Otherwise, they didn't seem to qualify for membership in the set of "beautiful people" who
congregated in the area each summer.

While the cottage had been a joint inheritance from the estate of their Grandmother Zachary, the Saunderses used it so much more frequently than Kyle or Drew that they had assumed responsibility for running the house. Though it was gracious, their style of living wasn't overly lavish—at least at Lake Geneva. They employed a live-in cook and a gardener, but Maureen did most of the housework herself with the occasional aid of a daily maid for the heavier cleaning and with help from her children.

Mitch was an executive with a well-known talent agency. Perhaps because he dealt with temperamental types in his work, he seemed unusually easy-going and low keyed. The only time Corey had seen him the least bit out of sorts was the evening before when Drew had been riding him for his refusal to represent the combo he played with.

Although they shared a quaint, flower-sprigged bedroom tucked away under the steeply sloping eaves of the house, Corey hadn't seen that much of Jan. Her half sister and Drew were too engrossed in one another to seek the company of others and they'd gone their own way. Arrangements for their wedding were progressing under Maureen's capable guidance. It was planned for the coming Sunday—only a week away. Once the wedding and reception were over, Corey would be free to leave.

As for Kyle, contrary to her fears that he might make her the object of his considerable sexual prowess, he'd mostly ignored her since their arrival. In fact, he had hardly seemed to notice her since the scene outside the restaurant.

Whether his apparent disinterest in her was only a cat-and-mouse move designed to encourage her to relax her guard again, Corey didn't know, but as a result of his lack of attention her fears had been allayed. She experienced twinges of panic only when she thought about the things he'd said after the dinner at Lorraine's, so she tried not to think of them at all.

Gillian Chalmers had returned from Chicago, and

Kyle spent most of his time with her. She was a cool blond post-deb, as glamorous as her name, whose parents had a summer home in the neighborhood.

Gillian's speech was accented by the broad vowels, strangled consonant endings, and zeed S's that were typical of alumnae of certain fashionable women's colleges. In her case, the cultured drawl was so exaggerated as to be laughable, and Corey once thought that she had detected suppressed amusement in Kyle's eyes because of it. But she had no doubt that in Kyle's estimation Gillian more than compensated for this affectation with her feline grace and striking beauty. What if she was shallow enough to boast that she wouldn't be caught dead wearing anything but a designer original? Corey was sure it wasn't her mind that attracted Kyle.

Because the adults at the Zachary home were otherwise occupied, she'd spent most of yesterday and today either on her own or with Greg and Betsy. She found the youngsters very entertaining. Greg was a strangely sophisticated and intense adolescent. In many ways he was a younger version of his uncle, but without Kyle's streak of cynicism. His sister, Betsy, was an enchanting little minx with huge gray eyes, round dimpled cheeks, and a sweetness of manner that was spiced by her fondness for mischief making.

There were so many wonderful things to do that time passed quickly. One could choose the pool or the lake for swimming; there was a croquet lawn; there were tennis and badminton courts, bridle paths, and hiking trails, and a golf course nearby. And, of course, there was sailing. This was far and away the most popular sport for the summer people.

The lake itself was lovely. It was spring-fed and bounded by rugged bluffs and magnificently wooded shores. Lured by its serene beauty, in the aftermath of the catastrophic fire of 1871, some the the most influential families of Chicago society fled the city. They'd developed palatial estates on the lake and the area began to be called "The Newport of the West."

After the income tax and the depression made such ostentation impossible, some of the more sumptuous homes had become private clubs or hotels, but by then Lake Geneva's attractions for vacationers had been firmly established. Many of the plush summer homes remained in private ownership and hundreds of more modest ones had been built. The hospitable tree-lined streets of the town proper slumbered through the off-season, and when, from June through August, the population quadrupled, they became prosperous beehives of commerce that catered to summer residents and tourists.

With a sigh prompted by her feeling of contentment, Corey tilted her head back and savored the sight of the white sails arching gracefully against the deep blue of the sky. She'd never before experienced a sense of being in such harmony with the wind, the water, the sunlight. The notion popped into her mind that this was how birds must feel—free of earthbound restraints, working with nature instead of beating the wings of their souls against the restrictions nature imposed. She thought she'd found her natural element and regretted that soon they would reach the dock and the day's lesson would be over.

Greg's muttering disrupted her tranquil mood and she looked at him over her shoulder. "What is it?" she asked. "Did I do something wrong?"

"Not you," he said emphatically, gesturing rudely toward the beach in front of the Zachary home. "I was just wondering what a neat guy like Uncle Kyle sees in a silly phony like Gillian."

Corey watched Kyle and Gillian strolling along the water's edge. One of his arms was draped across her shoulders while her arm was wrapped around his waist. Both of them wore bathing suits. Gillian's was composed of three skimpy triangles held together by strings. Around her waist was a belt of some gold-colored metal—maybe it *was* gold, Corey thought wryly—and this covered as much of her ample charms as the bikini.

Gillian might be a phony in some ways, but the nearly indecent skimpiness of her bikini left no doubt that her curves were real enough. She was certainly—Corey cut off her spiteful thoughts and hastily substituted—impressive!

"When you're older, you'll understand what he sees in her," she assured Greg.

He gave her a withering look. "For cryin' out loud, Corey, I'm not *that* dumb! Kids grow up a lot faster now than when you were young."

Choking back a laugh, Corey said, "I guess *you're* evidence of that, Greg."

Against her better judgment, she glanced toward Kyle and Gillian again. They had stopped walking and Kyle's back was toward them with Gillian partially hidden by his body. The boat was close enough to shore now that Corey could see Gillian's hand running indolently over the burnished skin of Kyle's shoulder before it trailed down the shallow indentation between the taut ridges of muscle on either side of his spine. Kyle's head was bent and they appeared to be— They were! He was *kissing* her.

Corey's stomach muscles knotted and churned. She longed to look away but found she couldn't. She watched as though mesmerized while the kiss went on and on, while Gillian's slim white fingers continued to probe the rippling muscles of Kyle's back.

Shivering uncontrollably, Corey relived the sensations that went with being the recipient of Kyle's kiss and not just an onlooker. She forgot her duties as Greg's crew. She didn't see the dock rushing up at them. She didn't hear Greg's instructions, much less follow them. When they'd almost reached the dock, Greg shouted a last-minute warning that stimulated a hazy response.

She got reflexively to her feet, assuming a half crouch that would enable her to cross from the port side to starboard, and at that instant the wind shifted and they jibed. The boom slammed across the cockpit, delivering a sickening blow to her temple as it swept her overboard.

At first everything was dark and cold. Then stars exploded in brilliant sparks against the blackness of her closed eyelids. Finally her body took over for her dazed mind and reacted with skills learned long ago and repeated often enough to become instinctive.

Squinting upward through partly open eyes, she pumped her legs, following the ray of sunlight that penetrated the tree-shaded water by the dock. Her lungs felt as though they would burst before her head broke through to the surface. She gasped for air and reached out to clutch the wooden piling nearest her. Weakly she began to work her way to shallow water.

Stunned as she was, she was aware of hearing laughter.

It wasn't Greg who was laughing. He was standing in the cockpit of the sloop and he was white-faced with concern.

"For cripes sake, Corey! I told you and told you— you have to concentrate every second when you're crewing for me."

"I think she's learned that lesson the hard way, Greg," Kyle said. "Lay off now."

The laughter continued, insistent and grating as a fingernail scratching across a blackboard.

She felt strong hands slide beneath her shoulders and knees and lift her effortlessly from the water.

It wasn't Kyle who was laughing. She looked up at him through water-spiked lashes as he carried her up the path to the house. His lips twitched a bit, as if he were controlling an impulse to say something, but he really looked quite grim.

"Kyle, darling," Gillian said in her best preppy drawl, "that was the funniest thing I've ever seen. The expression on Corey's face—it was absolutely priceless!"

Corey closed her eyes against the pain Gillian's shrill voice caused to rocket through the inside of her skull and burrowed her face into the sheltering curve of Kyle's neck and shoulder.

He smelled of sunshine and clover and his arms held her close, cushioned her, seemed to protect her from further harm. Despite her sodden clothes, she felt warm

and safe—and very sleepy. As she descended into the
blackness of unconsciousness, the last thing she heard
was Gillian's laughter.

CHAPTER
Seven

COREY SLEPT AROUND the clock. For the first several hours people kept coming in at intervals, calling to her until they'd roused her enough to answer them.

"Sorry, love," Jan explained after this had happened a number of times, "but we have to make sure you haven't done serious damage to yourself. Just respond somehow so we'll know you're only sleeping."

After that, she'd replied without ever waking up fully.

Toward dawn her sleep became fitful. She was disturbed by dreams in which she was running away from something or someone. Endlessly she ran, and though she never saw her pursuer she sensed that whatever it was she ran from was close behind and gaining on her. And she was so tired and her feet were leaden. She brushed the dream aside like cobwebs as she fought for consciousness.

When she finally opened her eyes, the first thing she saw was Betsy, who was watching her with round-eyed curiosity from the end of the bed. The little girl was sitting on her feet, which accounted for the last awful bit of her nightmare.

"Are you going to die?" she whispered.

"Not today," Corey answered solemnly.

Betsy gave an exuberant little bounce of relief and

Corey winced as, relieved of the constricting weight, the circulation returned to her toes with a sensation of needles and pins.

"That's good," Betsy lisped. "I had a turtle that died. I cried. I was only a baby then."

"Sometimes grownups cry, too, Betsy. Especially when they lose a pet or someone they love."

Betsy considered this momentarily. "Mommy helped me give a funeral for my turtle. She said he'd gone to turtle heaven, but he didn't."

"How do you know he didn't?"

"'Cause I dug him up," she said. Her face was enlivened by a mischievous, gap-toothed grin.

Corey stifled an urge to laugh. She should have known better than to ask that last question.

Betsy expected no comment from her when she slid restlessly off the bed and ran to the door. "Mommy told me to call her when you woke up," she said quickly before she disappeared into the hallway.

By the time Corey had bathed and eaten breakfast, she felt much improved, although her bruised temple throbbed. When Greg came in to see her, she was sitting up in bed, her head resting against the mound of pillows at her back.

"Sorry I yelled at you yesterday," Greg said shyly. He kept his eyes downcast until, shuffling his feet uncertainly, he raised them to look at her directly. "I really am."

"I know you are, Greg, and I'm sorry I fouled up. I hope your boat wasn't damaged."

"Nope. It didn't even graze the dock." His gaze settled on the side of her head. "Wow!" The exclamation was filled with admiration. "That bruise is a beauty!"

"I'll have to change my hairstyle so it's less noticeable till it fades."

"I don't suppose you'll want any more sailing lessons," he ventured.

"Would you give me more if I do?"

"Would I!" He brightened. "You bet I would, Corey."

"Then I didn't spoil my chances of crewing for you with my lack of attention?"

"Heck no," Greg said magnanimously. "I think you're a natural. You seem to have a knack for handling a small boat."

"That's all right, then, because I enjoy sailing and I'd like to have more lessons."

"Terrific! Er—umm—when would you want your next one?"

"What's wrong with this afternoon?"

"Wow, Corey! Not a darned thing."

After Greg's departure, she contemplated the closed bedroom door, bemused. His relief that she still wanted to sail in the races and his flattering enthusiasm over the idea of instructing her were balm for her tender ego. With her laughter, Gillian had wounded that as surely as the boom had bruised her temple.

In the early afternoon, she slept again. The weather had turned scorchingly hot, and Greg suggested that they postpone their sail until evening. When Corey finally came downstairs and entered the kitchen in search of a cup of coffee, she found Maureen was there consulting with Mrs. Bidwell, the cook, over menus for the coming week. While the wedding itself was to be catered, Mrs. Bidwell was in charge of preparations for the rehearsal dinner.

"You're an angel to do this for Greg," Maureen said to Corey gratefully, "but are you sure you're feeling well enough? The doctor advised us that you should take it easy today."

"It'll be good to be outdoors and I won't have to do anything very strenuous."

"The way Greg sails?" Maureen shook her head skeptically.

"Really, Maureen, I want to do this."

"You're sure you're up to it?"

"I'm positive. I just have a slight headache, and the coffee should take care of it."

"I don't mean to be a nag," Maureen said. "It's just

that we were all very concerned about you. Kyle was—well, I don't know when I've seen him so angry."

"Angry?"

"God, yes! He gave Gillian a real piece of his mind because she laughed when you had your accident. Poor thing. Not that it wasn't incredibly unfeeling of her to react that way, but she's so self-centered she hadn't a clue as to why Kyle considered her behavior offensive. She was terribly upset when she left here yesterday, and last night she must have phoned every ten minutes until Kyle finally got home from the DiLorettos' and they made it up."

Corey sipped her coffee and didn't reply. It was surprising news that Kyle had come to her defense, but having been subjected to his temper herself, it wasn't something she'd wish on her worst enemy. To her dismay, she realized she saw Gillian as an enemy, though she was reluctant to admit, even to herself, why she should.

Instead of cooling off after the sun had set, the temperature climbed. Late that night Corey lay on a chaise on the screened porch. The humidity was so high that a heat haze trailed ghostly fingers across the face of the moon and mist rose like steam from the lawn and flowerbeds.

When Kyle returned from his evening with Gillian, he drove around to the side of the house to park the Mercedes in a driveway opposite the porch. Obviously he intended to come into the house through this door. Corey watched as he skirted the grape-stake fencing that enclosed the pool. He stopped near the gate for a moment, as though debating the idea of having a swim. As he began walking toward the house again, she saw that he'd removed his sports jacket and carried it hooked over his shoulder. His necktie was off and he'd rolled back his sleeves. His shirt was unbuttoned almost to the waist and stuck in long damp streaks to his chest and shoulders and upper arms. Through the open front of the shirt, his skin shone with perspiration.

She held her breath when his steps sounded on the brick walkway leading to the porch stairs. Her heart fluttered erratically. She hoped he wouldn't notice her sitting in the darkness.

The hinges of the screen door squealed, then slammed behind Kyle, and he looked directly at her. Even in the shadows where she was sitting, her gauzy white beach jacket glowed in the dim light of the moon and gave her presence away.

"Corey?"

"Yes," she answered faintly.

Kyle threw his coat and tie over the back of a chair, then moved to the foot of the chaise and stared down at her. The scent of Gillian's perfume clung to him, permeating the air and assaulting her nostrils. She pressed her body more deeply into the lounger.

"What are you doing out here at this hour?" he asked softly. "Shouldn't you be sleeping?"

"I slept most of the day. Besides, it's too hot to sleep."

"Isn't the air conditioner working?"

"Yes, but I have a hard time sleeping in a closed room."

"What do you do in our subzero winters?"

"Suffer a lot."

His teeth gleamed against his dark face as he grinned. He sat sideways near her feet on the chaise so that he was facing her.

"You've been swimming," he said.

"Yes, awhile ago."

She felt the heat and hardness of his thigh next to her bare foot and shifted uneasily. She couldn't see him clearly, but she sensed his intensity.

"Did you have a good time tonight?" she asked quickly.

Kyle shrugged. He didn't look away. "It was a charity dinner-dance. Usually I make a donation and consider

I've done my bit, but Gillian wanted to go. You know the sort of thing."

She lifted her rounded chin proudly. "No, I don't, but I should think Gillian's company would be a guarantee of a wonderful time wherever you went. After all, it's not every man who can claim he's escorting the eighth natural wonder of the modern world."

Though he was silent, she felt Kyle tense through the sole of her foot, through the cushion of the chaise they shared. She felt the chill of his disapproval.

"I'm sorry." She issued the apology in a small voice. "I shouldn't have said that about Gillian."

"No, you shouldn't," he agreed coolly. "Not that it's any great shock to me that you don't like her. She wasn't very kind when you were injured. But at least her thoughtlessness wasn't premeditated."

"But I don't dislike her," Corey said rashly. "There's simply nothing there to dislike."

"Careful, kitten, your claws are showing," Kyle cautioned her silkily. "And if they weren't prompted by dislike, how would you account for your nasty comments about her?"

"I wouldn't even try, because I don't know why I made them," she admitted dully. "Even if I knew the reason, why should I tell you?" She ducked her head and concentrated very hard on arranging the folds of her jacket so as to cover as much as possible of her slender thighs.

"In that case, maybe I should explain to you why you're so catty about her."

He sounded so smug that Corey was coldly furious.

"If it isn't Gillian herself, it's just possible you're jealous of her possessions. Maybe she has everything you've ever wanted for yourself—expensive clothes, jewelry, cars, travel, servants, doting parents."

With each successive word Kyle spoke, the carefully erected barricade with which Corey had kept the truth from herself crumbled a bit and caved in around her, leaving her feeling raw and vulnerable.

God, she silently asked, how can he be so near the truth and at the same time so far away from it? Gillian had only one thing she coveted, but Kyle had not included himself in his list.

"You must wonder what Gillian ever did that she should have all that, while you—"

"You're wrong! I don't envy Gillian any of those things." Her voice shook with anger because he'd forced her to acknowledge the depth of her feelings for him. Swinging her legs off the chaise, she rose stiffly to her feet, every line of her body conveying hostility. "Why don't you just leave me alone!"

"With pleasure," Kyle snapped. Abruptly he stood beside her, his hand snaking out to grasp her by the upper arm and propel her toward the house. "But I'll see you to your room first. If you can't sleep, at least you should rest."

"No!" She protested so sharply that he stopped pushing her along in front of him and turned her to face him. "I c-can't go there," she stammered.

"Why?" The misleading softness of the question didn't completely veil the shortness of his temper at her continued resistance.

"Drew's there with Jan."

The last reaction she'd expected was that Kyle would smile and murmur with disarming blandness, "Poor Corey, left out in the cold again."

"What do you mean by that?"

"From what Drew's told me, this isn't the first time Jan has gotten her nose in the tent and wound up taking over the whole show, forcing you out in the process. Didn't much the same thing happen with your father?"

The velvety timbre of his voice sheathed a steely contempt that caused resentment to race through her nerve endings like wildfire. Inwardly she thought, Who the hell was he to pass judgment on a personal matter between Jan and herself? Biting back an angry retort, she replied stiltedly, "That was Vera's doing, not Jan's."

"Even so, it's amazing you feel any affection at all for your half sister."

"Not when you consider that by the time I was old enough to see what was happening, I was old enough to know it wasn't Jan's fault."

"How noble!" he said sardonically. "It seems you should be a candidate for sainthood after all—or for an Oscar."

"You know very well it's not noble at all. It's obvious you won't believe me, but I don't think being put in such a position has done Jan much good. I *had* to learn to be self-sufficient and that's a valuable lesson, so don't waste your crocodile tears on me."

"I wouldn't think of it." He started walking her toward the screen door. "Since you don't want to break in on the young lovers, I'd suggest another swim to cool your hot temper."

"But I don't want—"

He gave her arm a quelling squeeze. His hand seemed to burn into her skin through the thin material of her beach jacket and she tried to pull away from him, but he towed her along behind him and didn't even slow his step.

"I assume you have a bathing suit on under your robe."

She did, but it was the bikini Lorraine had given her and she felt exposed enough when she was with Kyle. She didn't want to double the sensation by showing herself in this skimpy thing! He left her standing near the bath house that he ducked into to change.

The underwater lights came on and the water beckoned her, blue and coolly inviting. The night was so hot that perspiration had gathered stickily at the small of her back and stung as it trickled down the sensitive hollow between her breasts. She lifted the weight of her hair off the back of her neck, but there wasn't the smallest movement of the heavy air to fan it.

Why not? she asked herself. Another swim would be heavenly and she could be in the water before Kyle came out of the bath house. She tossed her jacket onto a chair and dove in, relishing the feel of the cool water on her heated flesh. Her hair fanning out around her, she floated on her back and, with the slightest possible motion of her legs, began kicking toward the shallow end. She sat on the stairs with the water lapping about her shoulders, watching as Kyle came out of the bath house and did a running dive into the deep end of the pool. He swam the length of the pool underwater before he surfaced and returned to the other side with a powerful crawl stroke. He swam a number of fast-paced laps before he slowed, but Corey only watched. She was too comfortable to want to exercise.

"Now aren't you glad I made you come in with me?" Kyle called across the width of the pool.

"Yes," she called back. "It's wonderful."

He did a surface dive and approached underwater, lounging against the stairs when he reached them.

Without thinking of how it would sound, she said, "How surprised I am that you can be bothered by *heat.*"

"Ouch," he growled, but the throaty chuckle that followed said he wasn't the least offended. "I'm only human, Corey. Did you think a satanic guy like me would only sweat from the elbows down?"

"I guess I must have," she admitted. She smiled at him and he inhaled at the sight of her injured temple.

"You really got clobbered by that boom, didn't you?" Moving to her side, he bent over her for a closer look. "An inch or so lower and you'd have had one helluva shiner."

"It's all right now." She turned away, self-consciously covering the blemish with her hand, but he pushed her hand aside. Tilting her face toward his with his fingers cupping her chin, he lifted her hair out of the way to reveal the extent of the discoloration.

The bruise stood out darkly against the moon-bleached pallor of her skin, and he touched it lightly with one fingertip. When she flinched, his lips brushed her temple, offering feathery apology. Her velvety skin was sweetly assaulted by his lips, which traced the curve of her cheek to the corner of her mouth. He circled her gently with his arms and his mouth caressed hers tentatively, briefly, in a soft testing sort of kiss that ended almost before it had begun.

When he raised his head and looked down at her, his eyes held her own troubled, dilated gaze with a long drugging thoroughness that was agonizing in its impact. She felt that Kyle was reading in her eyes everything there was to know about her, that he had penetrated to her very soul. She was stripped of her last meager defense against him.

His hands played over her body, spanning her waist and gliding smoothly over her water-slicked skin, following the fine-boned wings of her shoulder blades, meeting above them to curve loosely around her neck. His thumbs lay along the wildly pounding pulses in her throat and held her chin immobile so that there was no turning back. Even had she wanted to, there was no escaping the tantalizing flurry of kisses that closed her eyelids, sampled the winging arch of her brows and the shell-like convolutions of one ear.

He had undone the narrow ties that secured the bikini bra and when his arms folded her close she gasped at the tingling sensation induced by the contact of his hair-roughened chest with her naked breasts. She sagged bonelessly against him, weightless in the water, and his mouth closed over her parted lips. There was no gentleness in this kiss; no allowances were made for her injured head . . . or her vulnerable emotions. There was only a primitive hunger in him that demanded her instinctive response to the heady sweetness of his probing tongue, to the feel of his body as he molded her ever closer to his taut thighs.

His hands seemed to be able to gauge precisely where to touch her to give her the most intense pleasure. Restlessly, recklessly, her own hands moved over the satiny coolness of his shoulders and back, cherishing his lean

Venus Rising

Kyle nuzzled her ear, his arms tightened their hold on her, and he whispered raggedly, "Have you any idea how good you feel?"

She buried her face against his shoulder, baring her neck for his explorations. He found the sensitive pulse point in her throat, the delectable little hollow behind her ear, teased them with the roughness of his beard and the tender moistness of his tongue.

"You are the softest woman," he marveled as though thinking out loud.

She was shaken by a tremor of delight that she was pleasing to him and she lifted her face from his shoulder, consciously inviting him to kiss her again. In that instant, she felt she would die unless he kissed her, and when he did she plunged wantonly into the fires of his ardor, moving her body in delicious provocation against his.

Corey was oblivious to everything but the ecstasy of Kyle's embrace. She was deaf to the warning creak of the screen door opening, then slamming as it closed. But Kyle must have heard. Raising his head to peer alertly through the slitlike openings in the fence, he muttered, "Dammit, it's Drew."

Corey's face was open, guileless, and glowing as she looked up at Kyle. His tender lovemaking had swept away the deeply ingrained reserve that had protected her for so long. His arms fell away from her, but she continued clinging to him until his eyes left hers. With deliberate insolence they raked over her breasts, making her suddenly aware of her nakedness.

"One advantage of making love in a swimming pool," he said flippantly, "there's a cold bath readily available in case of untimely interruptions."

That joking tone made her recoil as if he'd slapped her and she hastily turned her back to him. As she fumbled to retie the bikini bra, her head was bent forward, emphasizing the creamy fragility of her neck.

"It's a little late for modesty, Corey."

To Corey's ears Kyle's voice was brusque and uncaring. Her face burned with the heat of her angry embarrassment as she climbed the steps and retrieved her jacket.

"Drew probably won't stay long. Why not stick around? We can always pick up from where we left off after he leaves."

He was taunting her, demonstrating his power over her. Her face was flaming and she choked back an anguished sob. She brushed past Drew without speaking, blinded by tears, causing him to stare in surprise.

"Corey," Kyle called more loudly as she latched the gate behind herself. "Why not concede? Admit you've lost. There's no dishonor in being defeated by superior forces."

Jan was sleeping. Her pretty, pink and white face was scrubbed bare of makeup. She looked carefree and ridiculously young; hardly old enough to be a wife, let alone an expectant mother. Quietly Corey gathered up her night things and went down the hall to the bathroom.

There, under the fine spray of the shower, the tears came and the drumming noise from the running water camouflaged her sobs. But all the water, all the tears in the world would not be enough to wash away the anguish at her memories of Kyle's kisses—of his touch. Even now, when she knew it was part of his scheme to prove to Drew that she, too, had a price, she wanted his lovemaking. She wanted his love. She wanted to love him. *She did love him.*

Did that mean he had been successful, that he'd shown her that she could be "corrupted"? Or did it only mean that she was human?

How was she to fight back when he held all the weapons? With passionate ambivalence, she loved Kyle and she hated him. But she hated herself even more as, with a deep sense of shame, she admitted that in order for him to win his case, all he needed to do was give her enough rope and she'd hang herself.

The faceless, nameless, unscrupulous women who had "taught" Kyle from a young age to distrust love were detestable to Corey. They were largely responsible, she thought, for his philosophy of "be cruel unto women before they can be cruel unto Kyle."

Corey turned her face and her tears mingled with the cool spray of the shower. It was a long time before they were spent, leaving her drained and weary from the storm of emotion. It was ironic—God! It was a painful jest—that she, who had resolved to be restrained and frugal in giving affection, should squander her love with a spendthrift of a man who would call it counterfeit and throw it away.

CHAPTER
Eight

DAWN WAS BREAKING before Corey fell into a restless asleep, so it was understandable that she slept late the following morning. It was after ten o'clock before she dragged herself out of bed, and she was still sitting in front of the dressing table, listlessly brushing her hair, when Jan burst into the room with Drew close on her heels.

Through the mirror, Corey could see that Jan's face was like a thundercloud. Familiar with the signs, she knew that if the situation wasn't handled carefully, her sister's display of temper might soon deteriorate to the level of a tantrum.

"Please, babe, let's talk it over," Drew pleaded with Jan, his voice low and urgent.

"I'm sick and tired of talking and I'm sick and tired of you, Drew Zachary," Jan wailed. Throwing herself across her bed, she hid her face in the pillow.

Drew's expression showed clearly that he was bewildered and hurt. Corey hastily motioned him from the room, silently mouthing, "Let me talk to her."

Drew left reluctantly, and when the door finally closed softly behind him, Corey started to brush her hair again, watching Jan's reflection in the mirror. When Jan realized they were alone, she pulled a pillow from underneath the spread and hurled it angrily across the room, barely missing an antique porcelain vase.

"Dammit!" she shouted. "I could scream!"

"You *are* screaming, honey," Corey said calmly.

Jan's face crumpled and her bright blue eyes brimmed with tears, which brought Corey to the bedside. Sitting beside Jan, she touched her shoulder sympathetically and asked, "Do you want to tell me what the trouble is?"

"It's Maureen and the wedding," Jan said in a quavering voice. "She's taken over the whole thing and she won't let me have anything the way I want it. You know how we'd planned to go shopping for my wedding gown today."

Corey nodded.

Jan's pout became more pronounced. "Well, Maureen asked what kind of dress I'd like, and when I told her I wanted the traditional white with a train and a veil and everything, she was so—so disapproving!" Jan mimicked Maureen. "And she said, I hardly think that's suitable under the circumstances.'"

Jan scowled. "First she insisted we have the ceremony and reception here in the garden, then she limited the number of guests I can invite, and now this! And Drew goes along with whatever Maureen suggests. It's just too much!"

Jan looked appealingly at Corey, as though willing her to take her side in the matter.

But Corey wouldn't take sides. Instead she simply asked, "Do you love Drew, Jan? I mean, *really* love him? Because if you aren't very sure of that, you'd be better off not going through with the wedding. The ceremony itself is over in an hour or less. Your pregnancy will only last nine months. Eventually your baby will grow up and go out on its own. But, honey, if you love Drew, if you marry him, that's for the rest of your lives."

Jan was still frowning, but she didn't look sullen any longer. "I do love him, Corey," she said with quiet emphasis, "and I want to marry him more than anything."

"Then it seems to me that you should give him top priority."

"I know I should, and I try, really I do. It's just that it makes me so mad when Drew takes his sister's side against me."

"Have you talked to Drew about this?"

"Well—no," Jan answered hesitantly. "It seems so small-minded." She sighed heavily and plucked nervously at the white candlewick bedspread with her fingers. "I don't mean to cause friction between Maureen and Drew, but I suppose part of the reason I've objected to some of her plans is to test him. I want to believe he'd take my side if the chips were down, but I worry that he wouldn't."

"Maybe Drew isn't taking his sister's side in this, Jan. Have you ever thought he might have his own reasons for preferring a quiet wedding?" From Jan's expression, it was obvious that this had never occurred to her. "After all," Corey continued, "you are pregnant. It could be he's only trying to protect you from unkind speculation by keeping the ceremony simple and limiting your guests to family and the friends who are closest to you."

"Drew did say he wants a small wedding because he'd hate all the fuss of a big one." Jan's face was wreathed with a sunny smile. "He thinks the practice of spending a lot of money just to get married is barbaric and we should just put on our best jeans and find a preacher and go out for a pizza afterward! The only reason he's willing to compromise his principles is because he knows how much it means to me. And speaking personally, I'd hate for a lot of nasty-minded people to be counting the months on their fingers when our baby is born."

Suddenly unburdened, Jan jumped to her feet and danced lightly around the room. "And it will be lovely in the garden, won't it? The day lilies are in bloom, and the roses." She laughed merrily and threw her arms wide as she performed a graceful little pirouette. "I don't know what I'd do without you, Corey."

"In a few days you'll be married, Jan. You'll have Drew. Talk to him. Don't keep him in the dark about the way you feel. He was very upset when you refused to discuss this with him before."

"I will," Jan promised solemnly. "Poor Drew! I was so awful to him. I don't know what gets into me. Maybe I just need reassurance or something, but if you love someone, you should at least *try* to put their well-being above everything else."

"If you know that, Jan, you don't need me to advise you."

"None too soon, either! It's about time I grew up."

Corey shook her head as Jan's mood changed yet again. From bubbling optimism she shifted again to tears. Drew was going to have his hands full, Corey knew, dealing with Jan's volatile personality.

Jan came back to the bedside, dropped to her knees, and grasped Corey's hands tightly. "Corey, promise me that no matter what happens you'll stay on till after the wedding—just in case I need someone to give me a good swift kick and remind me of how much I love Drew."

Burying her face in Corey's lap, she went on tremulously, "I know it's silly of me—put it down to bridal nerves if you like—but I *need* you here. You're the only person I've ever felt I could rely on, however little I might deserve it. Just knowing you'll stand by me makes all the difference."

"Of course I'll stay, honey," Corey replied huskily. "Nothing could make me miss your wedding."

Corey had always felt that Jan could be the very model of diplomacy, if she put her mind to it. Finally dressed and downstairs, Corey learned just how true her intuition was on this point. Betsy was bubbling over with excitement because Jan had asked her to be in the wedding party.

Looking pleased with herself, Jan commented, "I don't know why I didn't think of it before. She'll be so adorable."

When Betsy had run off to her room to change so that

she could go shopping with them, Maureen said, "You're very sweet to ask Betsy to do this, Jan, but are you sure it's what you want?"

"Oh, yes!" Jan said without hesitation. She colored a little with embarrassment. "I'd like to be friends with you, Maureen, and show you I'll meet you halfway, but that's not the main reason. I think it will make the wedding more meaningful for Drew and me if Betsy participates."

They had discussed driving into Milwaukee, or even down to the Chicago area, to find dresses for the wedding, but Maureen knew of a specialty shop in Lake Geneva that might have something appropriate and they agreed it would be a good idea at least to take a look before traveling such a distance.

The store, Henriette's, was located in a group of shops that occupied the ground floor of a high-rise condominium on Lakeshore Drive. It was near the public marina and the long wooden pier that provided berthing space for the excursion boats that plied the lake.

Henriette's was not the kind of store Corey usually shopped in. It was decorated with the lavish kind of understatement that is very expensive to achieve.

Surprisingly quickly, they found the perfect dress for her role as maid of honor. It was a confection of raspberry chiffon over a whisper-slim shift of petal pink taffeta. The bodice of the dress was simply cut while the skirt was a romantic cascade of tiered ruffles.

Jan liked it so much that she chose the same basic design in a lovely ivory color. The floor-length gown was complemented by a lace-edged chiffon poncho. For Betsy they decided on a lace-collared taffeta dress in the same shade as the petticoat of Corey's dress.

"If it's a hot day, you're going to swelter in that taffeta," Maureen warned Betsy.

"I don't care, Mommy," the little girl replied dreamily, stroking the fabric with loving fingers. "It's so pretty."

Because Betsy was so entranced with it, Maureen

grudgingly approved of her choice. "I hope I don't live to regret this," she said. Holding up crossed fingers, she added fervently, "Pray it isn't *too* warm on Sunday."

They selected picture hats trimmed with ribbons that trailed down their backs to the hemlines of their dresses and even found matching pumps for Corey and Jan and patent leather "Mary Janes" for Betsy.

Despite her shock when she saw the amount of the bill for their things, Corey remained adamant in her refusal to allow Maureen to pay. She resigned herself to going lunchless for the next year to patch the hole this expense made in her budget as she wrote out a check.

Betsy grew more and more restive when they left Henriette's to visit other boutiques in the arcade where Jan carefully selected items for a small trousseau that was to be a personal betrothal gift from the Saunderses to her.

Maureen and Jan were enjoying themselves. They chattered about each possible purchase, and it seemed a shame that they were interrupted constantly by Betsy. The poor child was growing more and more bored by the minute.

After Betsy demanded to know when they would be through for the third time in as many seconds, Corey asked Maureen if she could take her across the street to the marina. She was sure they could find something there of interest to a seven-year-old.

"Would you, Corey? I'd be so grateful," Maureen said. "Isn't it funny what a difference a few years can make?" she asked in a whisper, casting an amused glance at Jan, who was assessing her appearance in a frilly brunch coat. "At seven shopping is boring; at eighteen it's beguiling."

Corey coaxed Betsy from beneath a display rack of swim suits where she'd been trying to entertain herself by pretending she was a bear in a cave. Predictably eager to abandon the shop and have a look at the boats, Betsy chattered gaily to Corey who'd collected all their packages. They strolled out into the sunshine.

Because the coming Friday was the Fourth of July, the flood of tourists visiting the town was nearing its crest. As they jostled through the throng along the sidewalk and across Lakeshore Drive to the beach, Corey held on to Betsy's hand, fearful they might become separated in the crowd.

Lake Geneva was busily preparing itself for the coming holiday. Crews of workmen were raising flags from every street lamp and installing red, white, and blue bunting on the dock railings.

The harbor itself was filled with hundreds of pleasure boats, and farther out was an even larger flotilla. Speedboats were planing and trailing foamy wakes of white in the deep blue of the water, while the sailboats moved sedately, mostly white-sailed, but some with rainbow-hued spinnakers raised. At the far end of the lake, in Williams Bay, the sage-green dome of the University of Chicago's Yerkes Observatory glinted dully above the trees on its ridge.

They passed several refreshment stands before they stopped at one that whimsically advertised, "No shirt? No shoes? No problem!" where Corey bought a double-dip chocolate ice cream cone for Betsy. Settling themselves at the end of one of the piers, they swung their feet over the sand with the sun warming their shoulders as they watched the workmen, the boats, and the crowd, enjoying the carnival mood of the scene.

Between the assaulting licks of her small pink tongue, Betsy divulged, "Mommy never lets me have chocolate ice cream away from home."

Forcing herself to smile, Corey said, "I can see why."

In the hot sun, the ice cream was melting rapidly. It was running down the sides of the cone and Betsy was already well smeared. She had a chocolate moustache and beard, and even a chocolate dot at the end of her upturned nose. Corey found it difficult to keep the little girl from becoming a total mess, and she was glad she'd had enough foresight to supply herself with plenty of paper napkins. She was relieved when the cone was finished, and she dampened napkins with lake water to clean up a very sticky Betsy.

It was while she was completing the mopping-up operations that Betsy suddenly cried, "Look, Corey! There's Uncle Kyle."

Starting, Corey quickly turned in the direction Betsy was pointing to scan the crowd. Because he was so tall, Kyle was easy to spot. He was just handing Gillian into the driver's seat of a white Jaguar sedan that was parked in front of a restaurant across the street. Before he closed the door, he leaned over and kissed her. It looked as though he pulled away and Gillian wound her arms tightly around his neck to prolong the kiss.

"Corey!" Betsy squealed. "You're squeezing my fingers so hard!"

"I'm sorry, honey. I didn't mean to hurt you."

"I know." Betsy nodded wisely.

In the next second, Gillian drove away and Betsy freed her still-grubby hand, waved, and shouted to attract Kyle's attention.

Impossible as it seemed, in spite of all the cars and people, Kyle either heard her call or spotted the wig-wag signals of her flailing arms and returned a wave. As he came toward them, Betsy ran across the sand to launch her small self at him. He scooped her up in his arms and laughingly planted a kiss on her cheek.

Leaning his head back in the tight circle of his niece's arms to look her over more closely, he teased, "What have you been eating, Miss Sticky Puss?"

"Anicecreamcone," Betsy replied quickly. She paused dramatically. "Guess what, Uncle Kyle!"

"What?"

"I'm going to be in the wedding! I've got a bee-yoo-tee-ful new dress, and I'm going to be a junior—a junior—" She looked beseechingly at Corey.

"Bridesmaid," Corey supplied woodenly.

"That's right!" Betsy confirmed, elated.

"That's great, sugar!" Kyle exclaimed indulgently. "You'll be the prettiest bridesmaid ever." He gave her another hug before he put her down and glanced quizzically at Corey. "From all those packages that Corey's guarding, it looks as if you've bought more than just a dress."

"I got a hat and some new shoes, too," Betsy said. "Is *she* coming to the wedding?"

"Who? Oh, do you mean Miss Chalmers?"

Betsy nodded.

"Yes, she is. Her family and ours are very old friends."

"But she isn't going to be *in* the wedding, is she?" asked Betsy, protective of her status and hoping for a negative reply.

"No." Kyle grinned down at her, but when he turned toward Corey, his smile faded. With perfunctory politeness, he asked, "Would you like a ride home?"

"Yes, please," Betsy said.

"I'm not sure—" Corey began weakly. She stopped to clear her throat. "I should probably stay. Maureen won't know where we are. She'll worry."

"Where is she?"

"We left her in one of the stores in the mall—'The In Thing.'"

"That's easy to fix then. I'll just go across and tell her you're coming with me."

"No, I—"

"I'd like a chance to talk to you privately, Corey," Kyle stated firmly.

They both glanced down at Betsy, who stood between them with her head thrown back, big-eyed and quiet as a mouse. She was following their conversation as if she were refereeing a tennis match. From her expression it was evident she sensed the antagonistic undercurrents of Corey's tension and Kyle's determination. Corey felt that unless she wanted to alarm Betsy, she had to go along with Kyle's request. After all, she'd have to be alone with him sometime, and it might as well be sooner as later.

* * *

Because Maureen had taken the family's station wagon for the shopping spree, Kyle was driving his sister's Mercedes. It was a tight fit for the three of them, and Betsy sat on Corey's lap for the trip home.

"Jan seems to be enjoying herself," Kyle said dryly and Corey agreed. This was the only comment he directed at her during the drive and she was grateful for his silence. But Betsy carried on a nonstop conversation with her uncle, telling him in extensive detail about her butterfly collection. Since the little girl was usually in motion, Corey was pleasantly surprised that today Betsy was content to sit quietly on her lap, resting her bright-chestnut head on Corey's shoulder, allowing Corey to become absorbed in the passing scenery. She couldn't bear to think about what Kyle wanted to discuss with her and she stared raptly down the leafy green tunnel of the roadway that was lined with huge old oaks and maples.

They passed one derelict mansion that gazed blindly at the highway through broken, ivy-trailed windows, but the more impressive summer homes were not visible from the road. There were a number of gatehouses, however, and their dimensions and styles of architecture offered silent testimonials to how very palatial some of the residences must be. Just the gatehouses looked like mansions—miniature mansions—as they bridged well-tended private drives, spreading a wing on either side like sentrybirds defending their nests.

As soon as they arrived at the Zachary home, Betsy deserted them to take her packages to her room and then find Mrs. Bidwell and have some lunch.

"I'm sta-a-arving," she cried as she charged up the stairs.

Corey took her own parcels from Kyle's arms. "I'd better put these things away," she said hesitantly.

He inclined his head in agreement. "I'll see you in the den in ten minutes or so."

She stowed her purchases, ran a comb through her windblown hair, and allowed herself a short respite in which to become more collected. It was nearly twice that length of time before she entered the den.

The family gathered most often in this welcoming walnut-paneled room. With its marine blue and white needlepoint rug, comfortable corner sofas, well-worn chairs, and wall units whose shelves overflowed with books and family mementoes, it was a cozy place to relax. Adding to its charm were mullioned windows offering views of the shady lawn sloping to the lakeshore.

"Help yourself to coffee," Kyle offered as she came into the room. "If you'd like something to eat, I'll ask Mrs. Bidwell to bring in sandwiches for you."

"Just coffee will be fine," she said, then poured a cup for herself. Her hand was none too steady and the cup rattled in the saucer. Even if she'd had any appetite, she felt that food would stick in her throat. Trying to seem nonchalant, she slipped her shoes off and curled up on the couch by the windows with her feet tucked under her.

Kyle remained standing near the well-stocked bar. His thumbs were hooked through the belt loops of his slacks and the sleeves of his shirt were rolled back to reveal the smattering of fine dark hair on his forearms.

His face was hard, eyes shuttered as he watched her take her first sip of coffee. He was so remote and impassive! It was hard to believe that only the night before he'd kissed her—that those arms had held her, that those hands—Corey caught herself up abruptly, before her straying thoughts could wander farther along that perilous path.

As he folded his tall frame into an easy chair, swinging one long leg over the arm, Kyle said, "I was pleased to see Maureen and Jan getting along so well today."

"From now on I think Jan will make more of an effort to be congenial," Corey said. "Maureen has been very understanding with her. I know all of you appreciate that being married will make terrible demands on Jan . . . on her ability to adjust. She's so very young. Drew has been wonderfully supportive."

Kyle nodded. "I'll admit that I've been surprised by

his patience. In fact, I've come to agree with you that he'll marry Jan, regardless of my guaranteeing them an income. That being the case, I've decided to continue his allowance."

Corey's eyes widened with astonishment. "That's very generous of you. It will mean so much to them not to have to worry about money."

"It's no big deal," Kyle countered. "If Drew is determined enough to go ahead and marry Jan without being certain of his prospects, far be it from me to discourage him. I'm only gratified to see that he's not allowing himself to be dissuaded. However, I don't plan to tell them till after the wedding, so I'd prefer that you not mention it."

"Okay."

"The only reason I've told you this is that since I've definitely decided what course of action to take, it supersedes our agreement. In these circumstances, it makes no sense to keep you here against your wishes. I'd be happy to drive you into Madison tomorrow, or even later this afternoon if you can be ready to leave that soon."

For a moment she was dumbfounded. She stared mutely at Kyle, thrown completely off balance by his unanticipated change of heart. If it had come only twenty-four hours earlier, his offer would have been a godsend, but now it was too late.

"Well?" he prompted impatiently. "If I'd wanted to, last night I could have shown Drew very graphically that you're as human as the rest of us. I assure you, there are no catches."

Her color high, Corey protested, "I didn't think there were, and I'm truly sorry, but I can't leave. I promised Jan I'd be here for the wedding."

Kyle got to his feet and strode to the couch, towering over her as he glared down at her angrily. "That's no problem," he said briskly. "It's only an hour and a half from Madison to Lake Geneva. We can easily arrange for you to return for the wedding."

"You don't understand. I gave Jan my word I'd stay *here* until the wedding."

"Then break it," Kyle advised curtly. "You can give her some excuse. Say you've been called back to work or something."

"I'm sorry," she apologized again, more stiffly, "but I can't do that." She replaced her cup on the cocktail table and rose. Since she had kicked her shoes off, he towered over her even more than usual. "It's terribly awkward. I realize that. But I believe Jan needs me with her just now."

"And self-sacrificing little martyr that you are, you can't bring yourself to let her down!"

Rankled, Corey lashed out, "Why do you find it so hard to accept the fact that I love my sister and care about her peace of mind, even to the point of setting aside my personal desires? You feel the same way about your own family."

"In case it's escaped your attention, Corey, there are quite a few differences between you and me." Kyle smiled grimly. "But whether you can't leave or *won't* leave, the outcome is the same, and I suppose we'll just have to make the best of the situation."

CHAPTER
Nine

IT WAS MAUREEN who came up with an idea for a simple hairstyle that would conceal the bruise on Corey's forehead. She even helped her make the change.

"This always looks so easy when Mr. Kenneth does my hair, but I'm beginning to see why I pay him so much," Maureen said doubtfully when she saw how shaggily she had trimmed the front of Corey's hair. "I'm afraid you're going to look like I've used pinking shears. Maybe I should have made an appointment with him for you after all."

Once Corey's hair was combed out, though, they decided they liked the style. The gamine cut of the bangs made her eyes look huge and brought out delicate hollows beneath her cheekbones she'd never noticed she had before.

"You've been hiding behind your hair, Corey," Maureen told her, and Corey cheerfully said, "Right on!"

Later in the evening, Jill DiLoretto phoned to invite Corey to attend Tony's exhibition the following morning. When the time arrived, Corey sailed confidently into the Windjammer Gallery and came face to face with a startled Jill, who evidently didn't recognize her at first.

"Corey?" she inquired. Her voice was shrill with

amazement as she studied the change in Corey's hair-style. Corey's confidence sagged.

"D-do you like it? What do you think of it?"

"Turn around," Jill ordered soberly, and when Corey responded with a hasty spin, she chuckled. "Not that way, silly! S-l-o-w-l-y."

When this had been accomplished, she answered the mute question in Corey's eyes, saying, "You look terrific you know. *Really!* The bangs are smart and sassy and, with the way your hair curls, they give you a very trendy look. It's just that, for such a slight alteration, they make you look so different. You'll take some getting used to."

"Good! That's exactly what I wanted."

"Which? Smart? Sassy?"

"Different!"

Jill cast an amused glance at her. "Now why would anyone as attractive as you want to look different?"

"I don't know," Corey replied wistfully. "It's just that I'd rather be better endowed and a little bit taller and a lot more sophisticated. I'd like to have sleek blond hair and green eyes—" Suddenly realizing how revealing this description was, she left the rest unfinished.

"So that's the way the wind blows," Jill quietly remarked. "You think you need to look like Gillian to compete for Kyle's affections. Well, you couldn't be more wrong, Corey."

"Please, Jill, I'd rather not talk about it. Could you ignore what I just said? Let's pretend I just walked in and look at the exhibit."

"If that's the way you want it," Jill agreed. "At least now I know why you have such an unusual expression in your eyes."

After this, except for her sailing lessons, Corey devoted the rest of Wednesday to trying to be useful. Wedding gifts were pouring in, and when she got home from the gallery she helped Jan list the ones that had arrived that day and write notes acknowledging them.

In the late afternoon and early evening, she transcribed some business correspondence for Mitch. He was supposed to be vacationing, but he seemed to pass most days closeted in his study, keeping track of one thing or another pertaining to his agency.

Since Corey's arrival he'd been complaining about how unreliable his secretary had become after the onset of her husband's illness. Now Mitch told Corey that his secretary had agreed to spend some time with him the previous week so he wouldn't fall too far behind with his workload, but at the last minute she had begged off.

"Shirley was absolutely incomparable before," Mitch explained. "She's old enough that she's not always flirting with my clients and she's discreet, tactful, and her secretarial and administrative skills are of the highest caliber. It's just since her husband had a heart attack that she's no longer very dependable." In a preoccupied way, he added, "I wonder if this job isn't getting to be too much for her."

Considering his easygoing disposition, Mitch was a surprisingly demanding employer. He scribbled in changes in the wording in most of the letters she'd done for him and even when she could have made the necessary revisions virtually unnoticeable, he insisted that the entire page be retyped. She'd never before worked for anyone who refused to sign a letter if there was so much as one correction. Even in the paralegal field, where accuracy was essential, such a degree of fussiness was unheard of.

When she handed Mitch the final drafts, keeping her fingers crossed that he would do no more editing, he read each one, word for word, before signing them.

"These are fine, Corey," he said after he'd proofread the first few. "You're extremely competent."

She sat across the desk from him, folding the letters and stuffing them into their envelopes as he finished with them so they could go out in the next morning's mail. When Mitch had signed the last one he leaned back in his chair and said, "I wonder if you'd be interested in coming to work for me. Not only do I like the quality of your work, you're an easy person to be around. I'd raise your present salary by half and the job has good benefits, besides which there's a generous expense account and quite a lot of travel involved. You'd enjoy that."

Corey didn't have to stop to think before she declined the offer. While Mitch might find her easy to work with, if today was a fair example, she had serious reservations about him as an employer. His current secretary must be a paragon! Even if it weren't for Mitch's nit-picking, she would never be able to square it with her conscience if she were to take advantage of such an opportunity knowing it had come her way primarily through someone else's misfortune.

Mitch took her negative reply with good grace. "I was afraid you wouldn't accept," he said, "and if the truth were told, I suppose I'm just as glad you didn't. Would you forget I even mentioned it?" He sighed, apparently suffering an acute attack of regret for his disloyalty in making the offer.

As Friday's races drew nearer, Greg's instruction in sailing became more and more concentrated. He even used some homemade buoys to mark out a course that they followed in a kind of dress rehearsal on Thursday morning. He'd taught Corey how to raise and lower the spinnaker and the balloon spinnaker. These were the huge, baggy headsails they would use to run before the wind if conditions were right, and he ceaselessly drilled her in handling them. He'd coached her in sailing theory and practices until they'd begun to function as a well-synchronized team. Sometimes she could even anticipate what his next move would be, and this saved valuable seconds when he called out an order.

Greg planned to pull the boat out of the water that afternoon. He was going to check the rigging and give the bottom of the sloop a thorough cleaning to remove any trace of marine grasses that had accumulated below the waterline. He wanted the hull to be smooth as glass in order to coax every bit of speed he could from it.

In the evening Kyle and Mitch would help him haul the boat to the yacht club marina and launch it there so that all would be in readiness for the races.

An oddly subdued Betsy was waiting for them at the dock when they returned from their final practice run late Thursday morning. She sat on a tree stump near the water's edge with her chin cupped in her hands, watching while they made the boat fast at the dock and stuffed the sails into their storage bags. Greg had special racing sails he would use the next day.

"Why the long face, Betsy?" Greg called to his sister.

"I don't have anything to do," Betsy whined, her expression doleful. "Mommy won't let me help her any more and Mrs. Bidwell said she'd skin me if I set foot in her kitchen again before the wedding, and none of my friends are home. Will you play with me, Greg?"

"Sorry, shrimp, but I have to get the boat ready for tomorrow."

"Can I help?" Her voice had assumed a wheedling tone.

"No!" Greg responded so adamantly that Betsy was more crestfallen than ever. Seeing this, he softened his approach and added in a kinder tone, "It's strictly a one-man job, Betsy. I'm so particular about the last-minute preparations, I never let *anyone* help."

Betsy turned the full force of her sorrowful eyes on Corey. "Would you play with me, Corey?"

Unable to resist such a brazen appeal, Corey said, "I'd be happy to, Betsy. What would you like to do?"

"Could we go on a picnic?"

Smiling, Corey agreed, "That sounds like a lot of fun," and Betsy's eagerness erupted until she was clapping her hands and fairly dancing up and down with pleasure.

Corey glanced down at her shorts and shirt. They were soaking wet from "hiking out," hanging far out over the gunwale to keep the sloop from heeling too much during the morning's lively sail.

"Just give me a few minutes to change my clothes,"

she said, "and I'll be right with you." Together they started up the path toward the house. "While I'm changing, you can decide where you'd like to go. But keep in mind it will have to be someplace within walking distance."

"I'll have to think about it."

Betsy's reply was so evasive that Corey studied her suspiciously as she ran ahead along the trail with skipping steps, taking sporadic swipes at the air with the butterfly net she carried. Betsy appeared so unconcerned that Corey was reassured the little girl had had no motive other than boredom in wangling her agreement to the idea of a picnic.

It was not until Corey came downstairs after changing into fresh shorts and a sleeveless scoop-necked blouse that she discovered how cleverly Betsy had manipulated her, for Kyle was waiting there with his niece.

"Uncle Kyle wants to go on a picnic, too," Betsy said cheerfully. "Isn't that neat?"

There was only one little problem, Betsy told them quickly. Mrs. Bidwell had threatened to injure the next person who invaded her kitchen, so there was no picnic lunch in the hamper. Kyle and Corey agreed that the cook had been so harried for the past few days with preparations for the wedding rehearsal that she might very well carry out her threat. Acting on the assumption that discretion would be the better part of valor, they took only the wicker picnic basket and a cooler that they filled with ice at a service station dispenser.

On the way to the Lake Delavan Park they stopped at a delicatessen. They bought crusty rolls, some bratwurst and potato salad, a few giant-sized dill pickles, a variety of cheeses, paper plates, and plastic knives, forks, and cups. From the liquor store next door, Kyle purchased a bottle of wine and some soft drinks, and at the last minute they passed a fruit stand where they added a basket of nectarines and another of cherries to their provisions.

"Isn't this fun," Betsy chirped encouragement to Kyle

and Corey as Kyle turned off the highway onto the narrow graveled road that wound through the park. "We'll have such a good time!"

They found a site that had a view of the water and was bordered by tall trees to give it an illusion of privacy. Kyle started the charcoal fire while Corey spread a cloth over the wooden table and began setting out the food, and Betsy went off with her butterfly net, waving it in response to Corey's request not to go too far.

"I didn't realize Betsy had asked you to come along today," Kyle said flatly.

"And I didn't know she intended to ask you," Corey countered warily.

"I think we've been had." Kyle's slow grin did funny things to her breathing and heartbeat.

"By an expert," she qualified. "Do you suppose Betsy comes by her talent for intrigue naturally?"

"It's a talent many females seem to have," Kyle retorted. "If I didn't know she was such a lone wolf, I might even suspect some kind of conspiracy."

"On the other hand," Corey parried, "she might have acquired her skill by watching you in action."

Kyle threw his head back and laughed heartily, and Corey found she was watching him with fascination. She registered everything about him—the way the muscles in his throat worked as he laughed, the lithe vitality of his body in comfortably faded, skin-tight jeans and a denim shirt left open to the waist. Her fingers itched to touch the soft shine of his dark hair where the leaf-filtered sun struck it.

She picked out one of the nectarines and bit into it, mostly for something to do for diversion from his compelling masculinity, and the fruit was in the perfect stage of ripeness—tangy sweet and peachily flavorful, cooling to her dry mouth.

"These are delicious," she said. "Have one?"

She offered the basket to Kyle. He took a rosy-cheeked nectarine and suddenly, with the juice of the fruit dripping between her fingers and threatening to run down her chin as she ate it, it seemed silly to try to remain distant or formal with him. If nothing else, she'd have today to remember.

She sat at the end of the bench where she could keep an eye on Betsy, who had struck up a conversation with another little girl, and watched Kyle as he grilled the bratwurst. When they began to sizzle over the glowing coals, the air was filled with the mouth-watering aroma of the broiling sausages. It wafted across the grassy open space to the play area where Betsy and her new friend were riding on the whirlagig and brought them running.

"This is my friend Andrea," Betsy introduced the freckle-faced, pigtailed little girl at her side. "She's camping here with her family. Can she eat with us?"

"If it's all right with her parents," Kyle answered, smiling at both girls before they hurried off to get permission for Andrea to join them.

Corey divided the pickles into smaller portions for Betsy's and Andrea's benefit, sliced some of the cheeses, and put servings of salad and a roll on their plates while Kyle poured wine for each of them and opened soft drinks for the girls when they returned.

When the sausages were ready all of them ate hungrily, not talking very much as they consumed the spicy brats wrapped in sourdough rolls, accompanied by the salad and the kosher pickles. The wine was a ruby Cabernet, fragrant and full-bodied, and even the plastic cup couldn't diminish its flavor or lovely color. Betsy and Andrea put away an enormous amount of food, and Corey ate with real enjoyment for the first time in several days.

"What is it about eating outdoors that makes everything taste so good?" she mused as she sampled a slice of creamy, slightly nutty Swiss cheese.

"The ants!" Betsy laughed. "That's what Mommy says. She says they're very high quality pro—pro—"

"Protein?" Kyle suggested. When Betsy nodded he grimaced and said, "That sounds like my ever-practical sister. She's given up trying to fight her children's unappetizing dietary preferences and has decided to join them."

"I think it's the dirt," Andrea chimed in. "That's what my mother says."

"My God," Kyle muttered darkly, "it seems to be catching."

The little girls were reduced to fits of giggles by his pretended repugnance for their eating habits.

"What do you think makes food taste so good on a picnic, Uncle Kyle?" Betsy asked.

"I think it's the company," he said softly.

"And I think all of you are right," Corey said lightly.

"Do we get a prize for being right?" asked Betsy.

"Yes! You may each have some dessert." Corey held out the fruit basket to them and after taking a handful of cherries, the little girls ran back toward the playground.

Taking his wine with him, Kyle left the table and stretched out on the grass at the base of an oak. He lay with his head propped against the bole of the tree, using his flat belly as a tabletop to hold the cup of wine.

Corey began wrapping the leftover food and storing it in the cooler, tossing the uneaten crusts of bread to a pair of bluejays that boldly waited nearby for handouts.

Studying his tented fingers that steadied the cup of wine, Kyle remarked, "I understand Mitch offered you a job yesterday and you turned it down."

Corey nodded. It hadn't occurred to her before that Kyle might be behind the offer, but now she wondered if he had been.

"I don't think he was very serious about it," she ventured.

"Oh, he was serious all right. Mitch takes his work too much to heart to joke about it."

"Anyway, I'm happy in my present job and I'm fortunate enough to be in the position of not actually needing the extra income."

Watching her thoughtfully, Kyle pulled a blade of

grass and chewed absently on one end of it. After a long silence he said, "I think you made a wise decision. Mitch is practically a workaholic. He'd run you ragged in short order."

"It surprises me that you seem to be able to put your own work out of your mind so well."

"You thought I'd be constantly keeping my finger on the company's pulse via long distance or something like that."

"Something like that."

"But you see, Corey, I don't live to work. I work to live, and I'm a great believer in delegating authority. When I was getting the firm back on its feet I worked more than my share of twenty-five-hour days because it was necessary, but that's no longer the case. Now I have a very capable management staff who seem to appreciate being entrusted with responsibility. I enjoy my work, but I also enjoy my leisure time."

Removing the blade of grass from his mouth, Kyle studied it as if he was startled to have found it there.

"The little imps have me doing it now," he commented wryly before he flipped it away. He finished his wine and got to his feet, dusting bits of leaves off his shirt.

"I think I'll go check on Betsy," he said as he loped off in the direction his niece had taken, leaving Corey staring pensively after him and thinking how effectively he'd compartmentalized his life.

He went with equal ease from being a tycoon to being a playboy, from family man to swinger, from enemy to lover. From woman to woman, she finished ruefully as she put the last of the food away and closed the lid of the cooler with unnecessary force.

She munched on a few cheeries and, sated with food, she sat on the grass where Kyle had lain, her back against the same tree. The bark was abrasive through the thin cotton of her shirt as she listened to the birdsong and looked up into the branches where a feisty red squirrel was bawling her out for daring to trespass on his territory.

She was almost asleep when Kyle returned. She was unaware he was beside her until he reached out and outlined her profile with his forefinger. When her eyes flew open, his face was so close to hers that everything else was blocked from view.

"You look nearly as young as Betsy and Andrea." He smiled as he softly touched her mouth. "Your lips are stained red by the cherries."

The objections Corey might have raised over his comment remained unspoken as his finger continued on its lazy journey, detouring to explore the fine arc of her collarbone before it resumed its downward course, following the rise of her breast to its crest.

"Please, Kyle," she entreated breathlessly, "don't do this." If he continued, she would be utterly lost.

"Why not? You want me to. Your eyes tell me you do." His mouth was so close that his lips brushed hers. His fingers moved over the sensitive bud of her nipple, nurturing it into full bloom. *"This* tells me you do," he whispered huskily, his breath mingling with hers.

He cupped her breast fully in the palm of his hand when he kissed her, but she managed to keep her lips from parting beneath the lighthearted warmth of his and he did not try to deepen the kiss. Somehow his restraint was more moving than if he'd persisted.

"Mmmm," he murmured when he had moved away from her. "You taste of cherries and wine, with just a hint of garlic."

His eyes danced wickedly and she pulled a handful of grass and tossed it at him, making light of her turbulent emotions by pretending to be offended.

"You're a heel, Kyle Zachary!"

He laughed outright. "That's not what most women tell me. In certain circles, I'm considered quite a romantic devil."

"Well, I'm not most women," she protested ingenuously.

"No. You're not, are you." He was suddenly serious

and reached out with one hand as if he would like to touch her again. "But at this moment I want you so much, I almost wish you were."

"At this moment I wish I were too."

"I get the distinct impression that you're not very open to persuasion. Is it because you haven't been with a man for a long time?"

She swallowed hard, trying to dislodge the panicky dryness in her throat.

"Corey," Kyle said softly, "am I right in assuming there hasn't been anyone since your husband?"

"You can assume whatever you want, but you've no right to expect an answer to such a question."

Her voice was barely audible and he leaned closer in order to hear her. She started to get to her feet, but his hand closed around her wrist, stopping her, keeping count of the rapid pulsations in her wrist with his fingertips. With his free hand he stroked her cheek and caressed the side of her neck as if he were taming a mettlesome filly.

"From that reaction, I'd say my assumption is correct."

"Why do you keep asking all these questions?"

"Because I want you to forget about your defenses when you're with me."

"But why?" The question rang with desperation. "Even if I forgot my defenses, as you put it, what's in it for you? Would you get some kind of charge out of it?"

"What I'd get out of it is *you*, Corey—stripped of your last reservation, right where I want you."

Frightened by his intensity, she pulled away from him.

"I know it rankled that I didn't make love to you that first day at the restaurant," Kyle added thoughtfully. "Now I think I should have. Maybe it would have made you grow up a little."

"Why didn't you then?" she asked hotly.

"Damned if I know. It just seemed like a good idea not to at the time." Shrugging, he continued, "Maybe it was because it was so obvious you hadn't had a lot of experience. You're about as vulnerable as they come, and I thought it would be dishonorable to take advantage of you when you were blinded by the heat of the moment. I was also afraid I might scare you off. Sure, I wanted you, but not on the basis of a one-night stand. I guess what it all comes down to is that I had this crazy idea that you were adult enough to make the decision for yourself, without being seduced or coerced into it. Obviously I was wrong."

Kyle's eyes were narrowed, measuring the validity of her response as he said, "Why not make it easy on yourself and tell me what you're holding out for."

"I'm holding out for something you'd never think of offering—*love!*"

"What if I asked you to marry me?"

For a timeless time, her heart seemed to stop beating. "I'd ask if you love me," she said at last.

He waved his hand airily. "I don't know what you mean by that, but I suspect you're confusing love with desire."

"No, it's you who're doing that. You once told me that because passion fades so quickly, love is relatively unimportant in helping a couple to deal with the problems that are inevitable in a marriage. Well, maybe you're right about passion. Maybe it doesn't last any longer than a head cold, but love can, and without love the smallest problem can be insurmountable. Love is the cement that bonds people together and makes them want to solve their problems."

"It may come as a shock to you, but I've heard that song before." Kyle shook his head dubiously and ran his fingers roughly through his hair. He was usually so free from nervous mannerisms that only this subtle clue indicated the forcefulness of his rejection of her interpretation.

"No sale, Corey," he said laconically. "I think that in your prudish little scheme of things, you're so tormented by guilt if you even want to go to bed with a man that you have to make yourself believe you're in love to salve your conscience."

"And I think you have a terminal case of sour grapes! Because you aren't capable of loving a woman you claim it doesn't exist."

His mouth twisted to a bitter line. "At least I'm not so repressed that I tie myself in knots for being human enough to have sexual needs and honest enough to admit it."

"That's certainly stating the obvious." Corey sighed resignedly. "I guess the picnic is over."

"Yes, Corey." Kyle's voice was hard and strangely threatening. "The picnic is definitely over."

CHAPTER
Ten

"HUSTLE, COREY, HUSTLE!"

The Frisbee had been captured by an errant gust of wind and was in danger of falling into the lake. Corey put on an additional burst of speed. By springing high into the air at the last minute, she managed to reach the Frisbee with her fingertips and deflect it enough that it landed safely on the beach. Amused by Greg's zealousness, she made a playful face at him before she leaned over to pick it up.

"Nice try," called Greg, giving her a sign with circled thumb and forefinger to emphasize his appreciation of her unstinting effort. "That was a lousy throw I made. Sorry."

As Corey straightened and prepared to make her own toss, she caught a glimpse of Kyle and Gillian on the terrace of the yacht club above the beach. They were standing with tall iced drinks in hand, chatting with Gillian's parents, and they were by far the most striking couple in the high-spirited holiday group gathered there. Kyle was magnetically attractive in fawn-colored slacks and a chocolate-brown shirt, and Gillian was chic and glamorous in a nautical white pant suit worn with a daffodil-yellow sailor's tunic. Ruefully Corey thought that if she were to wear white trousers, they'd become soiled somehow or other before she was out of the front door, but Gillian's were spotless after hours of wear.

Whether the unaccustomed pang of jealousy she felt in that moment guided her hand or whether what happened next was the result of pure chance, she'd never know. She released the Frisbee and watched helplessly as the fluorescent-orange plastic disc sailed high over Greg's head and into the crowd on the terrace, finding Gillian as its target. Aghast, Corey saw it strike Gillian's wrist, causing her drink to spash onto her silk-clad bosom.

For an instant Corey's feet felt as if they were embedded in concrete. Then they were free and she raced across the sand and up the grassy slope toward the terrace with a snickering Greg close behind her.

The crowd parted to allow them passage and, aware of numerous eyes upon her, Corey's cheeks were vividly pink when she approached Gillian.

"I'm dreadfully sorry," she said as her horrified gaze settled on the spreading brown Rorschachlike stain that was sharply etched on the yellow silk.

Gillian was practically emitting sparks, she was so livid. "You did that on purpose, you little bitch!" she accused nastily. "Look at this blouse. It's ruined."

Corey *was* looking—watching spellbound as a piece of chipped ice slid down Gillian's collar and was pulled by the force of gravity into the deep V of the blouse between her lush breasts.

"Oooh!" Gillian screeched. Her mouth was opened wide and her head was thrown back. Her hands were clenched tightly at her sides and she was quivering with rage. "I've never been so embarrassed in all my life!"

The ice chip had completely disappeared into the well of Gillian's cleavage, but it did nothing to cool her temper. She hurled a string of extremely unladylike epithets at Corey, most of which, while she might have seen them in print, Corey had never actually heard anyone use before. She almost admired Gillian's fluent command of obscenity.

"Settle down, Gillian," Kyle said curtly. "It's not the end of the world. It was an accident, that's all. After watching Corey throwing the Frisbee for the last half hour, I can vouch that from that distance she couldn't have hit you on purpose if she'd tried to."

"Please, Gillian, accept my apology," Corey inserted hurriedly as the other women's mouth closed with an audible snap. "I'm terribly sorry about your lovely blouse," she repeated. "I'll have it dry-cleaned for you."

Gillian's mother, Gwen Chalmers, a sweet-faced but colorless little dumpling of a woman, placed a fluttering hand on her daughter's shoulder in an attempt to calm her, but Gillian shook it off irritably. Her mouth opened and closed a few times, but no sound issued from her white-rimmed lips. Her eyes were glazed and bulging and her lovely features were so unbecomingly contorted by her fury that she reminded Corey of a landed fish gasping for breath.

Looking down at the unsightly stain and pulling the wet fabric away from her skin, Gillian wailed, "That was *tea!* I doubt that it will ever come out."

"Then allow me to replace the blouse for you," Corey said.

"Replace it!" Gillian echoed haughtily. "You couldn't even afford to replace the buttons, you little—"

"That's *enough*, Gillian," Kyle ordered firmly. "What's done is done, and continuing this unpleasant scene won't change it."

With Kyle supporting her on one side and Mr. and Mrs. Chalmers bearing her along at the other, Gillian was ushered smoothly away from the terrace through the French doors that led to the yacht club auditorium.

The dead silence that followed Gillian's exit was broken abruptly by the nervous chatter of many people talking at once to cover the fact that they'd been eavesdropping. Stimulated by having witnessed the rude exchange, the little knots of people returned to their own conversations.

"Gee whiz, Corey," Greg muttered, "why did you

have to fall all over yourself to apologize like that? It's not as if you did it intentionally."

Corey wished she were as certain of that as Greg and Kyle. As she bent over to retrieve the offending Frisbee, she sighed. "Poor Gillian. She was so upset."

"Ha!" Greg hooted derisively. "Gillian pulls a stunt like this over something or other at least once a month. She has no sense of proportion. To her, a run in her stocking is a major catastrophe! Now maybe we can figure she's gotten it out of her system for the rest of July and relax."

From the nearly imperceptible droop of Corey's shoulders, it was obvious to him that she was not entirely convinced.

"Why don't you come inside and wait while I find Dad and Mom and see if they're ready to leave," Greg said solicitously.

As she waited for Greg's return a few minutes later, seated on one of the leather sofas in an out-of-the-way corner of the auditorium, Corey thought wearily that it had been an eventful day.

It had begun with the color and pageantry of the parade of all the entries in the races that were scheduled for the day, escorted by some of the power boats in the yacht club fleet.

The races had been fun and exciting, and Greg had said that he was fairly well pleased with their second- and third-place finishes. He was a little dissatisfied with his own performance. He felt they could have won their first race if he hadn't been overconservative in plotting their course. A shift of wind direction had allowed another boat to round the last marker buoy while they were still tacking in order to be able to overtake it and approach the finish line on a broad reach.

Their loss had actually resulted more from luck than from greater wisdom or better seamanship, and Greg had accomplished his primary goal by maintaining his overall position in the summer-long competition for the Challenge Cup. He found that gratifying.

Following the races, there had been a barbecue. Dozens of chickens and two suckling pigs had been roasted to succulent perfection in huge metal troughs, along with yams and corn on the cob that were served dripping with melted butter. With servings of these complemented by a variety of salads, Corey had eaten until she felt she'd never be able to move again, and when Greg had suggested a game of Frisbee to work off the unaccustomed lethargy, it had seemed a good idea.

And it wasn't solely the soporific effect of too much food of which she'd wanted to rid herself. There was also the exasperation at being the victim of Gillian's condescension. Throughout the time they were sharing their meal at one of the gaily umbrellaed tables on the terrace, Gillian had interrupted every few minutes to introduce Corey to various members of the club. The superficial thoughtfulness of the gesture was ruined when, on each occasion, she referred to Corey as "the little secretary I told you about" or as "Greg's little crewman."

Finally it had become intolerable, and she'd jumped at the chance to avoid Gillian's patronizing behavior. Of one thing Corey was sure—Gillian would never risk the knife-sharp crease in her trousers or the shine on her handmade shoes by leaving the civilization of the terrace for the comparative wilds of the beach.

There was to be a dinner-dance at the club that night, but Corey had decided not to accept Maureen and Mitch's invitation to accompany them. Not only did she prefer to avoid Gillian, she assumed Kyle would be there as well. After the way he'd interrogated her yesterday and made his cryptic comment about the picnic being over, she felt as if she were treading through a minefield whenever he was near. Besides, she had to move her things into Betsy's room so Vera could double up with Jan when she arrived the next day.

Silently Corey promised herself that she would have a peaceful interlude that night. The weather had cooled and she'd be able to sleep without the suffocating stuffiness of closed windows and air conditioning. She'd move in with Betsy, but other than that the most she might do would be to wander down to the lakeshore where she'd have an excellent view of the fireworks display being put on by the town of Lake Geneva.

The evening did not turn out at all as Corey had envisioned it would. By now she should have known enough to expect the unexpected where Kyle was concerned, but she was speechless with astonishment when he joined Betsy and her on the beach. Since she planned to stay in anyway, she'd offered to supervise Betsy while she set off her small store of fireworks, and she was comfortably ensconced on the inflatable lounger she'd moved onto the sand, enjoying the little girl's "ooohs" and "aaahs" of pleasure as she marveled at the miniature starbursts emanating from her sparkler, when Kyle appeared out of the dusk.

Betsy was delighted and ran to him. "How's my favorite girl?" Kyle asked as he dropped onto the lounger at Corey's side to become the beneficiary of his niece's enthusiastic hug.

"I thought you were taking Gillian to the dance," Corey said stiffly when Betsy had gone off to run along the sand with a freshly lit sparkler.

"What gave you that idea?" He raised a quizzical eyebrow at her as he lay back on the mattress, folding his arms behind his head.

"I-I don't know," she stammered. In spite of his casual posture, she sensed a welter of suppressed emotions in the rigid control of his voice. Hurriedly she got to her feet. "Since you're here to oversee Betsy, there's no need for me to stay as well."

She didn't manage to take even one step before his hand shot out and closed around her ankle, hobbling her within its iron grip.

"There's every need, Corey," he said smoothly. "Think how disappointed Betsy will be if you leave before she's finished."

His fingers stroked, warmly persuasive, over her instep before his hand tightened and pulled her off balance, causing her to tumble back onto the lounger next to him. Not satisfied with this, he shifted position, arranging her so that she was lying close to his side with one of his arms around her shoulders, their hips and thighs touching. Her head was pillowed on his chest and she could hear the racing thunder of his heart.

"Just stay there and be still," he instructed her unnecessarily. She was too weak and totally lacking in the desire to move unless he willed it. As the evening progressed, the aerial rockets and Roman candles that exploded in the velvety darkness of the sky above Lake Geneva seemed tiny replicas of the fires Kyle ignited in her with his lightest touch.

At last the display ended and yawning sleepily, Betsy announced she was going back to the house to go to bed.

"I should go with her," Corey remarked. She stirred slightly, trying to rouse herself from her stupor and follow the little girl.

"No," Kyle said shortly. He refused to relinquish his hold on her. Instead of releasing her, his arm about her shoulders tightened while his other hand moved to her waist, half-turning her so that she was forced even closer to the hardening length of his thighs.

"Have you any idea of what you're doing to me?" he muttered hoarsely.

She held very still, unyielding to the ruthless pressure of his arms around her. "From the sound of your voice, I'm making you angry."

"Yes, dammit! I am angry. I'm angry as hell!" His eyes shone darkly, burning in their intentness as they probed hers. "I've always been the one who's called the tune in my relationships with women. I've been the one who's been in control. With you—" He shook his head as if to clear it. "I want to keep my distance and I can't. I wish to God you'd gone back to Madison when I gave you the chance!"

"Then let me go now, Kyle!" she cried.

"God help me, but I can't do that either."

The gentle night breeze, coming off the water, blew a tendril of her hair across his face where it clung to his skin like a sweet-scented web. "Corey," Kyle whispered thickly, burying his face in the fragrant cloud of her hair.

Her name on his lips was both an invitation and a plea, and the tension drained from her even as the soft sigh of his voice was picked up by the wind and borne aloft. It faded into the air, taking her feeble resistance with it, and she raised her lips to meet the heady ravishment of his.

He kissed her harshly at first, almost brutally, as if he wanted to hurt her—or himself. Then his mouth gentled and his hands moved over as if he were memorizing every curve of her body. He stripped her of her brief bandeau top with a deftness rising from desire, but his hands were shaking with impatience as they cupped her breasts, softly cherishing the rich weight of them.

Her hands had worked their way inside his collar to revel in the rugged width of his shoulders and now they were fumbling with the buttons on his shirt. She watched Kyle hungrily when he released her to pull off his clothes, entranced by his proud masculinity. His compelling pupil-darkened gaze skimmed hotly over her breasts and wandered upward to her face. When he met her eyes he read the desire plainly written there.

Sliding one arm underneath her, he arched her toward him with his hand between her shoulder blades. He moved slowly, deliberately, giving her time for reconsideration, giving her time for denial, but she could only surrender, and her arms opened wide to enfold him.

For a time he held her so lightly that the tips of her breasts barely grazed his chest, and she luxuriated in this tantalizing contact until, suddenly, he hugged her close, settling his full weight upon her and claiming her mouth with a ravenous abandon that approached desperation.

"God!" he groaned raggedly against her lips. "I'd walk through all the fires of Hell just to hold you in my arms."

The tortured admission seemed to have been wrung

from deep inside, and her arms wound around him convulsively, offering him the solace of her body. The last frail vestige of her resistance had vanished. If passion was all that Kyle could give her, she would become its joyful receptacle.

His mouth had left hers and was trailing hotly along her throat and across her shoulders to her breasts, following the creamy rise of one to its crest. He savored the ripeness of the nipple with the silky warmth of his tongue, teased it delicately with the rough edges of his teeth until it was impossibly swollen and aching. It had reached a state of exquisite sensitivity before his lips fastened around it to assuage the ache. He sucked it deep into his mouth before he repeated the ritual with the other breast.

His hands were feverish with eagerness as he opened the zipper of her shorts and reached inside the waistband to caress her intimately, and she was fluidly pliant within his embrace. She was utterly incapable of thinking when the quality of his kisses changed yet again.

Now he was demanding more than mere submission from her. He was touching her urgently, inviting her response, provoking it. His hands were searching gently or lingering boldly, exploring the most secret recesses of her body as if he would never know enough of her, and she was consumed by desire for him.

She drew him nearer, winding her legs around him and cradling him between her thighs, melting into his hardness as if she might make him part of herself by some sort of osmosis. She was open to him, straining to be even closer to him, and she welcomed the hard, seeking thrust with which he brought them together, abandoning herself to the wildly exciting sensations he was creating with each rhythmic caress, abandoning herself to the hot domination of his body and the taste of his kisses and the husky murmur of his voice as he urged her on to uncharted heights of ecstasy.

With his least movement, Kyle was generating a strange new tension deep within her, a need so devastating that Corey felt she might burst with the glory of it. Wave after wave of pleasure rushed through her, each one more intense than the one before. Her head was thrashing from side to side as she sobbed his name in the extremity of her rapture, but her cries were absorbed by his lips as he kissed her again, filling her mouth with the sweet searing plunge of his tongue. With a final, powerful surge of passion, they were transported beyond the highest pinnacle of pleasure, soaring together in a dizzying spiral of release that was stunning in its savage splendor.

"Corey," Kyle moaned. "My God, Corey!"

His breathing was raspy and labored as he collapsed against her. He was murmuring small endearments, and she bore the weight of his body gladly. She was replete with love for him, content to lie in his arms while the fires of passion dwindled to a languid afterglow.

After a while he eased away from her and rolled onto his back, but he continued to hold her close to his side, tucking her into the crook of his arm. He smoothed the damp, tousled curls away from her forehead so tenderly that tears rushed to the backs of her eyes. She hastily closed her eyelids in an effort to contain them, but they spilled through her lashes and trickled down her cheeks, their tracks gleaming silvery in the starlight. When Kyle felt their dampness on his skin, he wrapped both arms around her and dried the tears with kisses.

"God, but you're sweet," he whispered between kisses. "Soft and warm and small—so small to hold all of me." He rubbed against her in a sinewy caress, as if he would submerge himself in her softness. "You feel so damned good."

"Oh, Kyle, so do you!" Her hands stroked lovingly over the long clean line of his back. "I've never felt this way before," she admitted shyly. "I—it's kind of like dying and being reborn, isn't it?"

Kyle's arms tightened around her. His chuckle was a deep sensuous growl. "That's not a bad description, Corey. Too bad the French thought of it first."

She nipped at his shoulder in playful retaliation for his teasing. "Did they?"

"Um-hmmm." He framed her face between his palms, bringing his own face so close to hers that his mouth was only a whisper away. "They call it 'the little death.'"

"Clever people, the French," she breathed, arching her neck to kiss him lightly on the lips.

"Devilishly clever," Kyle agreed. When she would have pulled away, he stopped her by capturing her mouth, claiming it fully and deepening his possession of it. Their breathing mingled and quickened as he fitted the soft curve of her hips to the hard angles of his body.

They were so caught up in their delight with one another that Betsy's cry was repeated several times before either of them heard it. From somewhere on the trail above the beach, she was calling in a quavering little voice, "Uncle Kyle, where are you?"

For a moment Kyle was still. Then his muscles grew taut as he fought for control. In the next instant he had levered himself away from Corey. Bracing himself on one elbow, he raised to a half-reclining position and looked down at her.

"I suppose I'd better answer her," he whispered.

Corey nodded. "She really sounds frightened."

Smiling ruefully, Kyle turned toward the trail and called, "What's wrong, Betsy?"

"I'm scared, Uncle Kyle," the little girl replied. "There's a monster scratching at the window of my room, trying to get in."

"Don't be scared, honey," Kyle shouted. "Wait there. I'll be right with you." Lowering his voice, he commented, "Sounds like she's had too much Fourth of July."

He turned back to Corey and his eyes traveled over her, smoldering with suppressed desire. With a regretful shake of his head, he said, "I don't mean to imply you're not worth waiting for, Corey, because you are. I can't begin to tell you how desirable you are. But now that you know how fantastic we can be together, aren't you sorry you took so long to give in?"

Corey's ephemeral bubble of elation was shattered by the note of triumph in Kyle's voice. She sat up, hugging her knees close to her chest to shield herself, and watched silently as he hurriedly pulled on his pants. It was only when he leaned down to reach for his shirt that she inquired, "D-does this mean that you won't feel obliged to continue Drew's allowance?"

For a moment Kyle froze. Then he glanced at her and saw her modest posture and, surprisingly, he started to laugh. His laughter had a bitter ring to it, but it became apparent that his bitterness was directed at himself when he draped his shirt around her shoulders, buttoning it under her chin and arranging its folds to cover her nakedness as impersonally as if she were a child.

"I'm sorry you think I'd go back on my word," he reassured her gruffly. "I suppose I have only myself to blame for your asking that." He pressed her face against his shoulder for a few seconds before his niece called out again and he left her, saying gently, "I'll wait up the path with Betsy while you get dressed."

After he'd gone, it seemed to take an eternity to get into her shorts and bandeau top. She was all thumbs and she handled the garments as if they had changed somehow and were totally unfamiliar to her, when actually it was she who was changed. She knew that she had been altered in some vital, irreversible way by Kyle's lovemaking.

All the while she was getting dressed, her mind was racing relentlessly in circles, wondering how she was going to live with herself after tonight, wondering how she *could* live without Kyle. For she knew she must live without him.

She must never allow him to penetrate her defenses again. From the start she'd been like putty in his hands, but until tonight she'd experienced only Lance's inept demands on her body. For as long as she had only suspected the existence of the deep wellspring of passion that Kyle had tapped, she'd been protected by her own ignorance. Now that she and Kyle had been intimate, now that she knew how easily he could arouse her and how thoroughly he could satisfy her, it would be infinitely more difficult to keep him at a distance, but for the sake of her sanity, she simply had to do just that.

If Kyle were ever to make love to her again, she would be able to deny him nothing. He'd left her less than five minutes ago, and already she was sick with longing for him. How was she to get through the next two days without succumbing to her desire for him? And how could she face Kyle? Despite her misgivings about him, despite her protestations that she was "holding out for love," all he'd had to do tonight was crook his finger and she'd come running.

As it turned out, when Corey finally mustered enough pride and courage to join Kyle and Betsy on the trail, Kyle eased the strain for her, glossing over the situation by talking of inconsequential matters as the three of them strolled back to the house. He even produced a plausible explanation that satisfied Betsy's curiosity as to why Corey should have his shirt.

It was just as if nothing of any importance had occurred between them.

CHAPTER
Eleven

VERA KENYON WAS a petite, kittenish woman who looked much younger than her forty-two years. Unless, as in Drew's case, there was the advantage of wealth to be considered, appearances were vitally important to her; indeed, they were the only thing that really seemed to matter to her.

She went to great lengths to present an image of undying youth. Her style of dress, her use of cosmetics, the studious way she kept abreast of the latest fad, all contributed to the illusion.

She saw herself as a femme fatale and, on casual acquaintance, so had more than a few men. For a time, Corey's father had been one of them.

After Corey's birth, Laura Kenyon had been an invalid. Laura had suffered from rheumatic fever as a young girl, and the illness had left her with a heart ailment. Her doctors had advised her not to risk having children, and giving birth to Corey had proved to be too much for her frail constitution.

At the time of her mother's death, when Corey was a little over seven years old, Vera was already pregnant with Jan, and Corey had sometimes wondered whether her father would ever have married her stepmother if she hadn't been. Surely if he'd had time to get to know Vera better he would have seen some of the flaws in her character.

Foremost among these, in Corey's opinion, was Vera's penchant for drawing sharp-tongued verbal caricatures of people. She liked to sum people up in a few glib words, usually critical ones. Her favorite description for Corey's mother was "that selfish little frump." Corey had long ago been designated a "selfish, ungrateful brat." Vera labeled many people as selfish, possibly because she herself was so acquisitive.

Vera felt she'd found her rightful niche in the company of the Saunderses and the Zacharys. She arrived on Saturday morning along with Anson Stevens, an old friend of Tom Kenyon's who was an honorary uncle to Corey and Jan and who was to give Jan away at her wedding.

Vera was so elated over her daughter's marital prospects that she even behaved cordially toward Corey. What this amounted to was that she ignored Corey rather than subject her to a barrage of insults once she'd made a waspish comment about Corey's new hairstyle.

"Hasn't anyone told you, dear? The hungry waif look is passé," she advised spitefully.

If Corey had ever had any inclination to envy Jan, the fact that Vera was her mother would have dissuaded her. Even on the eve of Jan's wedding, Vera treated her as if she were six years old. She scolded her for her behavior, for her conversation, for things she'd done and things she hadn't. She all but checked to see if her daughter had cleaned her nails and washed behind her ears.

Now that she was so close to being freed of Vera's nagging on a regular basis, Jan was good-naturedly tolerant of it. She even laughed about it with Drew.

Why Vera should act the eternal mother with Jan was an enigma. She had no particular liking or affinity for children. She alienated Betsy and Greg with her fishy stare and tactless comments before she'd been in the Zachary house for an hour. Betsy was admonished for being heard as well as seen, and Greg was advised he would ruin his posture if he didn't sit in his chair properly.

It was apparent she hadn't noticed that Maureen and Mitch encouraged their children to express themselves, and that Greg was at an age where he naturally preferred to keep his feet propped higher than his head.

Though she often offended others, Vera was virtually insult-proof. In the case of Kyle, however, she more than met her Waterloo.

Since she fancied she was irresistible and she obviously found Kyle the same, Vera draped herself all over him from the moment of her arrival. When she sat next to him at the luncheon table, she persisted in her laying on of hands, unscathed by his milder rebuffs. At last, fed up with her gropings, he peeled her hand off his thigh and looked at it as if he were identifying an especially distasteful lost object. Returning it to her lap, he said coldly, "Madam, I believe this is yours."

Corey colored with embarrassment for Vera, and Drew covered his appreciation of Kyle's squelch with a cough, but Jan choked on her consommé until she had to excuse herself and leave the dining room.

In the afternoon several of Drew's fellow musicians arrived. They were going to provide music for the ceremony and reception, and they conferred with Jan and Drew over their selections. Drew was the butt of a good deal of friendly ribbing, among other things over the neat appearance of his hair and beard. He'd had both of them trimmed and tamed.

After his friends' temporary departure for their campsite at a state park a few miles away, Corey helped Drew string Japanese lanterns about the swimming pool in preparation for the prenuptial festivities. She held the ladder steady, handed him whatever supplies he needed for the job, and generally kibitzed. It was the first opportunity they'd had for a private conversation in the week of their stay.

"I want to thank you for standing by when Jan needed

you," Drew said gratefully. "It's been kind of rough for her and I know it's meant a lot to her that you've been here." He ignored the quick, self-deprecating hunch of Corey's shoulders. "You know I'll take very good care of Jan, don't you, Corey?"

"Yes, Drew. I know you will." She was touched by his earnest acceptance of responsibility.

"We both have some growing up to do, but both of us recognize it, and I figure as long as we do it together, we can't go too far wrong."

She handed him the orange lantern he indicated he wanted next.

"It's made a big difference to me that Kyle and Maureen have been so helpful," he said, standing back a bit to get a better perspective on the color mix of the lanterns he'd strung so far. "I think maybe a yellow one now," he added, and when he'd moved the ladder and was again perched at the top of it, she handed him one.

"How have you and Kyle been getting along?" he asked offhandedly. "I was worried after the other night at the pool. I thought I might have interrupted a disagreement. Then Kyle clammed up over it—"

"We've gotten along well enough," she interrupted hastily. "I like your family, Drew."

"They like you too, Corey." He grinned happily down at her. "Greg and Betsy think you're the greatest thing since sliced bread. I'm relieved you haven't fallen for Kyle though. I'm afraid he'd be more than you could handle." Drew sighed deeply. "It's turned out to be a very good week. I'm glad Kyle suggested we spend it here. I'm really going to miss him while he's away."

There was a small silence while she handed him a lime-green lantern, then an amber one. "Kyle is going away?" she inquired faintly.

"Yeah. He's leaving for the West Coast tomorrow night after the reception. He's decided to take a chance at opening a chain of retail outlets that will sell smaller models of computers for people to use in their homes, and he'll be staying long enough to get the first couple of stores established—six months or so. Kyle says it's the wave of the future and I tend to agree with him. By the end of the decade, I think the work-saving convenience computers can offer will be fairly well accepted by the general public. Already grade-school children are at ease operating them. Eventually they'll be as common a household appliance as—well, as dishwashers."

Drew continued on in this vein and Corey's replies must have been cogent enough because he didn't seem to notice anything unusual about them. Inside, though, she felt shaken and dazed.

Here was further proof, if she needed it, of how little Kyle cared for her. He was leaving tomorrow, he'd be gone for months, and he'd never even bothered to mention it.

Face facts, she told herself fiercely. The only attraction she might have for Kyle was a transient one at best, and then, in all likelihood, only because she hadn't succumbed to his charm the moment they'd met. Much as it hurt, the sooner she accepted that, the sooner she could begin to put the shattered pieces of herself back together.

It hurt even more when Gillian wandered down to the pool while Corey was clearing away debris and the unused decorations and revealed that she was accompanying Kyle on his trip to San Diego.

"So you see, Corey," Gillian drawled smugly, looking like the cat who'd gotten the canary, "all your silly efforts to worm your way into Kyle's affections have come to nothing."

The comparing look she gave Corey's slight, jeans-clad figure was less than flattering. "I don't know why you'd ever have thought you could compete with me. I mean, just look at yourself! You're so unfeminine. Next to me you look like a boy! You've been such a nuisance that if you weren't so pathetic, you'd be a colossal joke."

Corey withstood Gillian's contempt stonily. "If you plan on marrying Kyle, I'd advise you to cultivate more than your sense of fashion."

"Oh, but I have Corey, dear. Believe me, I have,"

Gillian purred. "Kyle has made it abundantly plain he much prefers me *an naturel.*"

Beneath her breath, Corey muttered, "I'll bet you even have a designer's label tatooed on your fanny."

"What was that?" Gillian hissed.

Refusing to be the one to back down, Corey met the rancor glittering in Gillian's eyes with her own stalwart dark-blue gaze. The pupils in the other girl's eyes contracted until they resembled pinpricks in the hard green of the irises as, in dulcet tones, Corey repeated her statement loudly enough that Gillian could not fail to hear her.

"Why, you little bitch!" Gillian shrieked.

Before Corey could guess her intentions, Gillian had given her a surprisingly powerful shove that toppled her into the swimming pool just behind her. When Corey surfaced, she noted with satisfaction that the windmilling action of her arms and legs at the moment of her impact with the water had created a splash large enough to thoroughly soak the front of Gillian's green silk-jersey dress. Gillian brushed at it ineffectually, near tears with frustration.

"Now look what you've made me do," she bawled illogically before she turned and stalked away from the poolside and through the gate.

Accepting her dunking philosophically, Corey paddled back and forth a few times before she clambered out of the pool. The cool swim was actually very refreshing after the grubby work of putting up the lanterns and the heated argument with Gillian. As she sat on the tiled edge of the pool kicking her feet in the water, she smiled broadly. It had been worth it, she decided—more than worth it!

For no good reason, Corey's mood of lighthearted recklessness persisted while she showered and changed into dry clothing. Since it was almost six o'clock and Father Milne, the Episcopal priest who was to perform the ceremony tomorrow, was due to arrive for the rehearsal, she slipped into the turquoise and cream caftan.

She added a trace of lip gloss and some eyeshadow. Now that her bruise was hidden by the bangs, with her skin tanned to a toasty golden brown and the pink flush of anticipation glowing beneath the smooth curve of her cheekbones, she needed no other makeup.

After brushing her hair until it was glossy and sleek, dusted here and there with sun-lightened streaks of dull gold, she caught it up and back at the sides with small combs enameled in turquoise and dark blue. She slid her feet into high-heeled sandals, and she was ready.

When she arrived downstairs, she found that Kyle was alone in the den. After a momentary hesitation, she entered the room. It was the first time they'd been alone since last night.

"You're looking pleased with yourself," Kyle observed as he came to her side at the corner windows to hand her a glass of sherry.

"It's a happy occasion," she answered, smiling up at him engagingly over the rim of her glass. She tried to ignore the tingle of excitement he'd generated in her fingertips where his hand had brushed hers. "Where's Gillian? I saw her earlier and I thought she'd gone to find you."

"She went home to change her dress," Kyle said dryly. "She told me you'd purposely splashed her. Is that why you're looking so satisfied?"

"I splashed her, but inadvertently." Corey left his question unanswered.

"Tch, tch!" Kyle shook his head with disbelief. "Two accidents in as many days. That's a rather large coincidence."

"Yes, isn't it?" Corey agreed evenly. "Perhaps Gillian is accident prone. Perhaps I am. Who knows?"

Kyle's eyebrows rose eloquently. "From what I've seen of you, I wouldn't be surprised to find out it was you."

"And you've seen enough of me that I haven't any secrets from you, have I?" She managed to keep any tinge of resentment or embarrassment from her voice and the question came out throaty and seductive.

"Are you flirting with me, Corey?"

She lowered her eyelids with a slow flutter of lashes and favored him with a sexy sidelong glance as she sipped her sherry.

"Surely, Kyle, a man with your vast experience should know when he's being flirted with."

"So it would seem, but I've made the mistake of judging you by the same criteria I'd apply to other women once too often."

"Thank you," she returned hesitantly, "I think."

"Oh, that was a compliment, all right," he said softly, "and you're most welcome."

"Since it's apparently honesty time, I'll admit I was flirting." She met his eyes squarely, without coyness.

"You needn't resort to that bag of tricks, you know." He returned her gaze with brooding intensity. "As a matter of fact, it would be a very good idea if you didn't. You're skating on dangerously thin ice without resorting to such womanly wiles."

Her bravado exhausted, Corey blushed and turned quickly away from him. Standing close behind her, Kyle removed the forgotten sherry glass from her fingers and set it aside. His hand traced the curve of her waist through the sheer fabric of the caftan, moved down to the flare of her hip, then stroked from the hollow of her spine upward, coming to rest at the nape of her neck.

She swayed against him, breathless and weak-kneed under his touch. Through the window, she saw a long black sedan disappear down the driveway on the other side of the house.

"That was Father Milne's car," Kyle whispered close to her ear. "You lead a charmed life, Corey Kenyon. Once again the cavalry has come to your rescue in the nick of time, right on cue to prevent your unconditional surrender."

He laughed, but there was a humorless, unpleasant edge to it. "You're so easy to read, I can almost see the wheels spinning in your head with confusion. Let me assure you, after the way you responded to me last night it would be less than honest to deny that I know I can take you physically whenever I choose to, but what about your mind—your heart?"

So he didn't know quite everything there was to know about her! He didn't know that almost from the beginning she had capitulated to him in every way but the ultimate physical one. And before last night that had been avoided only by the intervention of Drew and the grace of God.

Kyle's fingers curved warmly around her neck and slid under her chin to tip her head back into his shoulder.

"How do you feel about last night, I wonder," he murmured. "Relieved? Frightened? Hungry for more?"

Did he expect her to come up with an answer to that; to try and package her chaotic emotions in a single neat, polite descriptive phrase? Closing her eyes tightly to hide them from his scrutiny, she replied in a choked voice, "As you said, I'm confused."

"I'm leaving for Southern California tomorrow night. I'll be there for several months. You could come with me," Kyle suggested in an offhand way. "They tell me you can sleep comfortably with your windows open year round out there."

Corey's eyes flew open and she found the strength to pull away from him.

"No," she replied flatly. "I can't do that."

"It's evident your alleged confusion doesn't lead to any uncertainty over that decision."

He sounded angry. She rubbed her forehead with one trembling hand and kept her back to him. "Isn't Gillian enough for you?" she retorted.

"What the hell does Gillian have to do with us?" he asked sharply.

"She told me she's going to San Diego with you."

"She's going, but with her parents, not with me. Her father is a partner in the business venture I'll be working on." He turned her to face him with one hand on her shoulder. His mouth was unsmiling, but his eyes were crinkled with amusement. "There's nothing between

Gillian and me, if that's what's holding you back."

She started to reply, but Kyle touched a silencing finger to her lips.

"Don't say anything now." His voice was rough with urgency. "Think about it for tonight and give me your answer tomorrow."

CHAPTER
Twelve

THE GARDENS WERE lovely in the long shadows of twi-
light. As Jan had observed, the lilies were in full bloom,
glowing exotically orange and yellow, backed by the
cool blue through purple hues of delphinium. There were
bright clusters of gaillardia and calendula that were bordered by cushiony tufts of alyssum, and the fragrance
of those tiny white blossoms vied for heady supremacy
with the scent of the roses.

It was just after nine o'clock and soon it would be
fully dark. Already the Japanese lanterns around the
swimming pool shone jewel-toned, like small cheerful
beacons. Most of the younger crowd had gathered around
the pool where Drew's friends were playing dance music.
The band had set up their instruments in front of the bath
house, and from her chair on the porch, Corey could see
that Jan was seated close to Drew as the combo played
a subdued jazz rendition of *Stardust*. The soft, breathy
notes of the clarinet lead echoed poignantly on the night
air.

"Drew is really quite talented," Anson Stevens remarked.

"Yes, he is," Corey agreed. Tilting her head to one
side, she studied Anson's craggy-featured face. His
ruddy skin was heavily lined, but his eyes were as bright
as ever beneath his dark shaggy brows, and his salt-and-

pepper hair was as thick as a twenty-year-old's. He had the kind of profile that would not look out of place carved into a mountain; not so much handsome or even heroic, and certainly not regular, but full of character.

In the years since her father's death, Corey had had few opportunities to see Anson, and she was glad that he was here now—especially now. She was content to remain at his side and she wasn't the least bit tempted to desert the group of older people on the porch for the merry-making at the pool.

Anson sighed contemplatively. "I don't know where the time has gone. It doesn't seem possible that little Jan is getting married tomorrow."

"I know what you mean." Corey smiled, fondly recalling a much younger Jan who'd had no time for dresses or other girlish fripperies, and absolutely no time for boys; a ten-year-old tomboy with scabby knees and lightning bugs in her pockets and braces on her small, pearly teeth.

"It's too bad Tom couldn't have lived to see her wedding. He would have been so proud of both of you, Corey. I know it may be difficult for you to accept, but in his own way your father loved you very much."

Puffing absentmindedly on his pipe, Anson fell silent, leaving Corey to consider this claim. There had been a number of occasions when she'd had cause to think her father's indifference to her might be a sham. There'd been a time when he had slipped a few extra dollars into her hand when she'd left home to do some shopping, another when she'd found a birthday card with a sentimental verse stuck into her dressing table mirror, a few times when he'd looked at her with a furtive expression of tenderness or pride.

Aloud she said, "Yes, Uncle Anson, I suppose he did."

"Neither Tom nor I were very good at expressing our love."

"Were you ever in love?" In spite of her effort not to show that she was astonished by the idea of the self-contained Anson Stevens being in love, it was manifested in her question.

Chuckling appreciatively, Anson chided her, "I wasn't always an old fogey of fifty-eight, Corey!"

"It's not that. It's just—"

"I know, my dear." He patted her hand affectionately. "You don't need to explain. By now I hope I see myself with enough objectivity that I can understand why you'd be surprised to learn I'd once been in love. What the hell! It even surprises me, come to think of it.

"But when I see a beautiful young woman like you sitting with the rocking-chair set when you should be with the young folk dancing the night away, it causes me some concern. I can't help but feel partly responsible. Your father and I were the men closest to you in your formative years, and neither of us was a shining example of manhood."

"How can you say such a thing! You were always wonderful to me!"

"Maybe," he said doubtfully, "but I opted against having a normal family life and your own home was far from typical, and I think it's time you knew how it all came about." His eyes were veiled by a plume of smoke as they traveled over the delicate cast of her face. "You're very like your mother, Corey. It takes me back to see you. God, but it's tragic Laura didn't live to raise you."

He was silent for a time, apparently caught up in his memories, but she didn't intrude on his reminiscence. Because Laura Kenyon had been bedridden for the last several years of her life, Corey's own memories of her mother were hazy at best, but she cherished them. Her throat had filled with a hot well of tears at the mention of Laura's name, and she waited quietly for Anson to continue.

At last he said, "The woman I was in love with was Laura."

Corey started and turned to stare at him and he smiled gently at her. "Your father never told you, did he?"

"N-no, he didn't."

"Tom and I had been friends from the time we were in high school and in a number of ways we'd been friendly rivals before we met Laura. At first our rivalry over her was friendly, too. Then, when each of us had come to love her, it stopped being friendly. At least for a while it did.

"After you were born, when Laura was so ill, we became close again, and I think it helped her to know she hadn't come between us. Your father loved her deeply, Corey. Never doubt that. It may be that he never stopped loving Laura."

"But he had an affair with Vera while my mother was still living," Corey said bitterly. "That would be easier for me to forgive if it had arisen from an abiding love for Vera, or even if they'd had a great romance. But it was only lust."

"Don't be too quick to minimize the power of physical needs as a driving force," Anson cautioned her bluntly. "Sometimes they can be more compelling than any other motivation."

She averted her head and murmured, "I know." She ought to, she added to herself with silent vehemence.

"Have you ever thought that his extramarital affair with Vera may have been your father's means of running away from the fact that the woman he loved was dying?" Anson's sorrow was clearly delineated on his weathered face. "I lived through that awful time with him, Corey, and because I loved Laura, too, because Tom and I were so close, I know that's all it was. An escape.

"Your mother knew it, too, and she never held his infidelity against your father. The only reference she ever made to it, to my knowledge, was one night when I became angry because Tom had gone out and I believed she needed him there with her and she said, 'Sometimes when a person is behaving the least lovably, it's an indication that they need more love than ever.'

"And the saddest thing of all is that Tom never came to grips with his loss. He kept on running until his dying day. That's part of the reason he kept his distance from you. As you grew up, you reminded him more and more painfully of all he'd lost."

"And you, Uncle Anson?"

"I ran in my own way, Corey, only my escape was inwardly directed. I built a shrine to Laura inside myself and worshiped at the altar of my love for her. I guarded it closely and never opened my heart to another woman, and that was an excess of grief that Laura would have hated."

He took Corey's hand in his and gave her fingers a warm squeeze. "So you see, in our individual ways, both your father and I let Laura down. She risked *everything* for love—you're living proof of that. She knew the danger to herself if she became pregnant, yet she took the risk because she believed a person is only half alive if she isn't willing to gamble to attain her desires.

"She would want her daughter to be the kind of woman who would open her arms and her heart and invite love into her life. The kind of woman who loves passionately and generously, who receives love gracefully, joyfully."

Involuntarily Corey scanned the crowd at the swimming pool until she saw Kyle. He was dancing with one of Jan's friends, his head held at an arrogant angle, his body moving with supple masculine grace in rhythm to the Latin American beat of the music. His raw sexuality was so potent, even at a distance, that her heart raced and her breathing quickened with excitement at the sight of him.

"What if the love you give isn't reciprocated?" she asked in a low, tormented voice. "What if it isn't even wanted?"

"You're referring to Kyle Zachary, aren't you?"

"How did you know?"

"I have eyes in my head and I've known you from childhood, my dear." Smiling down at her, he went on, "I don't want to advise you as to specifics because, in the long run, you're the only one who can decide what's best for you. I also know how terribly hurt you were when Lance Gilchrist left you, but I would like to give you something to think about, and it's simply this—as painful as it can be to love unwisely, it's infinitely more painful to withhold love. If you suppress love, it turns sour. Deny it and it can become so caustic that it eats away at your soul until all that's left is an empty shell and an emptier life."

Suddenly unable to bear the melancholy underlying Anson's mood, Corey remarked lightly, "That's certainly a profound statement, but I'm not even sure I'm cut out for the love and marriage bit." She grinned impishly at him. "Vera says she doesn't care if I marry a dozen times, she'll still be convinced I'm a born spinster."

"You, a spinster!" Anson let out a peal of laughter and caught her close in an enveloping hug. "Corey, speaking as a man of some experience who still has a connoisseur's appreciation for beautiful women, I hope I'm *never* too old to be capable of recognizing that you're a young woman who's eminently well qualified for love and marriage. The fact is, I've never seen a less likely candidate for spinsterhood."

CHAPTER
Thirteen

"CAN YOU SEE him, Corey?" Jan asked anxiously.

By standing on her tiptoes, Corey was able to peek through a convenient gap in the hedge behind which they waited for the processional to begin.

Folding chairs had been arranged on a carpetlike sweep of lawn, and the wedding guests were seated at either side of a white-runnered, ribbon-cordonned aisle. She could see beyond them to the little rise beneath the maples that Jan and Drew had chosen as the green cathedral for their exchange of vows.

Father Milne, his rotund body made regal by his gold-trimmed vestments, stood facing the aisle. His back was to a simple, birch-wood altar, and Drew, Kyle, and Hal Dickinson, a friend of Drew's who was a groomsman, were on his left.

For a heart-stopping moment, Corey's gaze dwelled on Kyle—tall, broad shouldered, and lean hipped, his tawny skin Indian-dark by contrast with the dove gray of his jacket and vest and the crisply pleated white of his shirt front.

"Well?" Jan hissed impatiently. "Can you see Drew?"

Turning her attention to Drew, Corey answered, "Yes, I can."

"How does he look?"

"Why, Jan, he looks so"—at a loss for words, she paused before finishing—"so urbane."

Surely that epitome of tailored elegance couldn't be the Andrew Zachary she knew; he of the strategically patched overalls and leather sandals. She should have guessed yesterday when she'd seen him with his beard trimmed so neatly and his hair slicked down rather than standing out wildly as it would, but she was hardly prepared for the sight of the well-groomed young man awaiting his bride beneath the trees.

Somewhat bemused, she added, "He looks very handsome."

"Doesn't he look at all nervous?" Jan persisted.

"Yes, he does a little. He's a bit on the pale side and rather solemn."

Jan giggled. "Good! It's awful of me, but I'm so relieved I'm not the only one with butterflies in my tummy. After grousing about wanting a big church wedding, now I wish we'd eloped!"

Turning, Corey hugged Jan hard. Her eyes grew misty as she looked at her sister. She was so radiantly lovely in her wedding dress.

"You're beautiful, Jan," she whispered. "I'm so very happy for you and Drew."

Jan scowled at her. "Don't you dare to start crying, Corey. If you go all to pieces, I will, too—I just know it—and my mascara will run. Thank God Kyle is Drew's best man! He's so cool. Maybe some of it will rub off on the rest of us."

Cool, Corey thought. The lacy brim of her hat shaded her face as she bent her head to study the fragile straw basket of summer flowers she carried.

Yes, above all else, Kyle was cool. "I want you," he'd said. "Come with me." Without a word of love on his part he demanded that she surrender all of herself to him—heart and mind, body and soul.

No! Don't think of Kyle, she told herself firmly. She had resolved not to give him any space in her thoughts until the wedding and reception were over. She had avoided being alone with him and postponed the moment when she'd have to tell him she wouldn't be going with him to San Diego, postponed finalizing her decision to return to the quiet haven of her own cloistered life.

The trio of flute, clarinet, and guitar had completed the prelude and the baroque, stately chords of the processional hymn wove their magic on the balmy summer air. Corey smiled reassuringly at Betsy, who was proudly waiting to lead them down the aisle. She glanced over her shoulder at Anson, strong and distinguished in his tuxedo, and was briefly taken aback by the worried expression she thought she saw in his eyes. But she must have been mistaken, for his smile was quite carefree as he ceremoniously placed Jan's hand in the crook of his arm.

"Ready, Jan?" he asked, giving her hand a calming pat.

"As I'll ever be," she replied. "Let's go."

Corey nodded to Betsy, signaling her to begin, and as Betsy stepped out from behind the hedge, Corey followed her erect, oddly dignified little figure across the grass and down the aisle.

The wedding service was old-fashioned and familiar, yet at the same time it was stirring and highly personal. Corey was caught up in the reverence of the ritual—standing, sitting, sometimes kneeling on the white cushions that had been provided for the wedding party.

When Jan repeated her vows, her voice low but even, Vera began crying, and the loudness of the sobbing shook Corey out of her trance. That was when she sensed that she was being watched closely. Looking past Jan, past Drew, she found that Kyle was studying her. A smile tugged at the corners of his mouth when he saw that she was returning his glance.

Tearing her eyes away from his, she bowed her head so that all he could see of her face was the lower part of her profile, but she was unable to recapture her enchantment with the service.

When the dismissal sentences had been pronounced and the music of the recessional soared forth in celebration, her hand was unsteady when she placed it on Kyle's arm. He pressed it close to his side for an instant, and the protectiveness of the gesture surprised her.

Throughout the time immediately following the ceremony, while they posed for the photographer, their respective roles dictated that she should be separated from Kyle by the bride and groom. And when they took their seats at the head table in the pavilion the caterers had installed for the wedding breakfast, she was careful to keep her distance from him.

A number of people had proposed toasts before Hal Dickinson, who was seated next to Corey, got to his feet to offer his. Grinning irreverently at Jan and Drew, he said simply, "May all your troubles be little ones."

Someone added loudly, "Hear, hear!" and in the general laughter and applause that followed, Jan blushed prettily. Raising his glass to her, Drew remarked, "I'll drink to that!"

The band began playing on the patio, and there was an exodus of guests in the direction of the music. Corey took advantage of this opportunity to escape to Betsy's room and repair her makeup.

She had already packed her things and arranged to return to Madison with Anson and Vera. When the time came to leave, all that remained for her to do was to change from her dress into the clothes she'd left out.

Her hands were shaking so badly, it took several tries to apply lip gloss without smudging it. The moment of truth was almost at hand—the time when she must confront Kyle and tell him that she wouldn't be accompanying him to San Diego. She'd do that the first chance she had, before her courage totally deserted her.

When she answered the knock at the door, she was startled to find Kyle leaning lazily against the doorjamb.

As he entered the room and closed the door behind himself, he drawled, "Were you going to skip out without saying good-bye?"

"No, of course not."

Looking up at him from under the brim of her hat, she was impressed by how very big he was. It seemed to her that he filled Betsy's room with his sheer size and the magnetism of his presence. She backed away from him until she was stopped by the corner of a dresser digging into her spine, but he followed, maintaining an overwhelming closeness to her.

"Why would I do a thing like that?" she asked tremulously.

"Beats me, but the way you've been avoiding me last night and today, I thought that might be your intention."

Averting her face, Corey fixed her eyes on the boutonniere of lilies of the valley in the buttonhole of his jacket.

Obviously annoyed by her timidity, Kyle requested explosively, "Will you please take that stupid hat off so I can see you properly?"

Her head jerked up and she glared at him. "It's not a stupid hat!"

"No, it isn't, is it," he agreed, defusing her anger. "It's lovely and you're lovely in it, but let's get rid of it anyway."

Adroitly he removed the long, pearl-studded pin that secured the hat, lifted it from her hair, and sailed it across the room onto a chair. Thus freed, his hands grasped her upper arms. While she stood wide-eyed with amazement, rendered speechless by his actions, he gave her a not-too-gentle shake and, at the same time, in contradiction to the punishment his hands inflicted, his eyes caressed her face.

"Oh, Corey," he groaned helplessly as he pulled her into his arms, holding her with his cheek pressed against hers, "I swear, I don't know whether to put you across my knee or kiss you! What am I going to do with you?"

"You're not going to do anything with me, because I'm not going with you to California." The crossness of her words was muffled by his shoulder.

"I know you aren't," he acknowledged dryly. "You've

made that fairly obvious by being so damned elusive."
He rocked her slightly to and fro in the tight circle of his
arms. "For such a sweet-appearing little thing, you can
be as stubborn as a mule."

"Stubborn! Me?" Her voice squeaked with disbelief.
"When it comes to being stubborn, you make me look
like a piker."

Her hands were wedged between their bodies and she
eased them upward to his shoulders in order to try to
push him away, but she succeeded only in being drawn
closer to him. His hands were spread hotly on her back
and he was crushing her to the hard wall of his chest,
holding her so close that her heart seemed to beat in
unison with his.

Now that she'd stopped struggling, he teased the sensitive skin of her neck with little biting kisses until, of
their own volition, her arms were entwined about him,
her fingers curled ecstatically into the thick springy hair
at his collar. Her head rolled limply to one side to give
him access to the pulse that fluttered erratically in the
hollow of her throat. He touched the tip of his tongue
to it, and the sensation this evoked caused her to shiver
uncontrollably.

"We'd better stop before this gets out of hand," Kyle
said hoarsely. "You're shaking all over."

"So are you," she returned breathlessly.

He laughed roughly and loosened his arms to hold her
lightly, with his hands linked at the back of her waist.

"The difference is, I don't try to deny that I want
you."

"I'm not denying that I feel the same way," she said
weakly.

"Then why won't you come with me?"

"I just can't." She trembled again, this time with
dread. "You frighten me, Kyle."

His mouth tilted in a half smile as his eyes wandered
over her features. "I know you're afraid, Corey, but it's
not me you're afraid of. Desire isn't a disease, you know.
It's a very natural thing. And making love isn't fatal. In

fact, after the other night, I'd think you'd admit that with the right person it can be quite beautiful."

"Don't make fun of me! You know very well it's the emotional consequences I couldn't cope with. It's hard enough to walk away from you now, Kyle! If I had an affair with you, I don't think I'd be able to survive the ending of it."

"I know." Still smiling, he relented. "And since you feel so strongly about it, would it make any difference if we were married?"

Her gaze faltered and she looked down at her fingers, which were nervously smoothing his lapel, toying with the lilies. The flowers were crushed now from their embrace. Their perfume came off on her fingertips.

"Is that a hypothetical question?" she asked.

"No, Corey, it's a serious question." He rested his forehead against hers. "I'm asking you to marry me."

She raised her eyes hopefully to his, finding them near—so near—and filled with tenderness. Hesitantly she asked, "Do you love me?"

Removing his hands from her waist, he thrust them in his pockets and moved a step away from her. His smile was gone and his expression was bleak without it.

"I don't know," he said, brutally direct. "I don't know how this so-called 'love' usually affects a person. All I can tell you is that I care about what happens to you. I want you and I want to be with you, and although I've tried, I haven't been able to find an antidote that would help get you out of my system. Since it seems to be a chronic condition, I'm willing to make a promise of permanence and faithfulness to you, and I'm prepared to do everything in my power to make our relationship a success. That's something I've never even been tempted to do before."

He grimaced ruefully. "You see how well you've turned the tables on me—I was supposed to be the one to convince you to sell out, and instead it's me who's going against my fundamental beliefs."

"You s-sound so resentful."

"Do you blame me? I saw what blind adoration did to my father and it wasn't very pretty."

For long moments Kyle was silent. His eyes were opaque and unseeing, and Corey knew he was reliving the horror of his father's suicide. Then, with a start, he returned to the present, saying bitterly, "If you're wondering if the way I feel about you has made me inclined to reduce myself to groveling and pleading, the answer is no! I've asked you twice now and I won't ask again."

"What your proposal amounts to then," she said numbly, "is an ultimatum."

"From my point of view, it's more in the nature of a compromise."

"How can you compromise over a thing like this? Either you love someone or you don't." Her eyes appealed mutely for understanding. "I'd like to say yes, Kyle, but I can't. Not on such an uncertain basis. How can I be sure that eventually you won't meet a woman you truly love? I rushed into one marriage, and it was a disaster! I never want to go through that again. Maybe if you'd give me a little more time—"

"Time!" he interjected sharply. "God, but you're such a child! I've paid you the compliment of being honest with you, but what you seem to want is a lot of romantic moonshine wrapped up in a pledge of undying devotion. Apparently you have a fuzzy-minded notion that a declaration of love guarantees some kind of fairytale ending, that it confers immunity to unpleasantness or pain."

Shaking his head pityingly, he turned brusquely away from her. As he strode toward the door, he said, "Sorry, Corey, but that's not a very realistic expectation. Love won't pay the rent or keep the baby in shoes."

He reached the door and paused. With his hand on the knob, he turned to face her.

"Do yourself a favor," he said harshly. "Admit that your reluctance to come with me is caused by your insecurity. Admit that you're stopped by a fear of your own feelings as much as by whatever doubts you might have about the constancy of mine."

Although she longed to call out to Kyle, to run after him and stop him from leaving her, Corey remained silent. As he left the room, she was frozen by inertia.

What was holding her back? If she hurried, she might still be able to catch up with him before he'd returned to the reception.

Her pain-darkened eyes focused on the boutonniere. The lilies of the valley had fallen from Kyle's lapel and been trampled underfoot. They lay on the carpet, bruised and already yellowing. She sank to her knees beside them, picked them up, and touched the sweetness of the petals to her mouth. When she moistened her lips, she tasted the nectar of the lilies that clung to them.

What was stopping her? She closed her eyes and saw Kyle's face. She re-created his tender expression.

Except for the words themselves, he had offered her everything she'd ever wanted. All she'd have had to do was reach out and claim it. And he was right. She'd been too afraid to take the chance.

CHAPTER
Fourteen

IN THE WEEKS that followed Jan's wedding, Anson Stevens spent several evenings with Corey, and eventually she told him enough about what had happened between Kyle and herself that he could guess the rest. It was Anson who forced her to fully appreciate the value of what Kyle had offered her; what in her irrational fright she had permitted to slip through her fingers.

"He may not have said so in as many words," Anson pointed out, "and from what you've told me about his father, I can see why that particular phrase would stick in his throat, but there are times when actions speak louder than words, Corey. It seems to me that Kyle demonstrated he loves you by his actions. He cared about you enough that he wanted what was best for you. Lord knows he could have lied. In your frame of mind, you'd have believed anything he chose to tell you, but he wanted you to come to him like an informed, responsible adult—and if that's not love, I don't know what is!"

"I'd like to believe you," Corey said, "but the truth is, Kyle seemed almost hostile. And besides, why should he love me when he can have his pick of any number of women?"

Anson sighed. "I'm beginning to understand first hand why Kyle was so angry with you! Modesty is all very

153

well and good, Corey, but there are times when your humility is absolutely maddening. It's no wonder you have trouble coming up with the right answers when you persist in asking the *wrong* questions! The question is, 'Why shouldn't Kyle love you?'"

"Well, you're certainly not doing my self-esteem any good with all your criticism!" The droop of her shoulders expressed her dejection as she added, "It's a moot point, anyway. I had my chance with Kyle and I let it pass me by."

Trying to lighten the burden of her despondency, Anson said, "Maybe it's not too late."

"Kyle's been gone three months now and I haven't heard from him. If he cared about me at all, surely he would have seen to it that some contact remained between us. Drew says Kyle's not much of a letter writer, but he calls regularly, so I know he's been seeing a good deal of Gillian."

"Gillian's not his type," Anson replied dismissively. "Kyle's not the kind of man to be satisfied with a clothes mannequin, no matter how attractive she is. Anyway, I think he'd leave it to you to make the first move."

"Me!" It was clear that Corey was nonplussed by the suggestion. "I just couldn't."

"What have you got to lose? As it is, you're only making yourself miserable over him. Besides, Kyle is a proud man, and you've already turned him down twice—which is one more time than a less confident man would have given you a crack at. So it's not likely he'd give you a third chance unless he had very good reason to think you'd changed your mind."

In the following weeks, Corey worried about what Anson had said. She knew he was right. She'd seen only that Kyle was handsome, virile, and sought-after, and her lack of faith in her own ability to hold the interest of such a man had dulled her perceptiveness to the extent that it hadn't even occurred to her that her refusal of his proposal might have hurt him in any way. Naturally she knew that men were not any less susceptible to rejection than women, but till now she'd never thought of what she'd done as a rejection of Kyle.

Over a month had gone by before Anson asked her one evening if she'd ever gotten around to writing Kyle.

"No, I haven't," Corey replied.

"Is it because you're not convinced I'm right?"

"It isn't that," she answered lamely. "I've tried writing to him, and my letters all turn out so stiff and formal that I just haven't sent one."

Anson studied her so keenly that she knew he'd seen the color fluctuating in her cheeks. She was looking entirely too wan lately.

"What you need is something to break the ice," he advised. "Christmas is coming up. Why not send Kyle a card?"

"I'll think about it," she promised noncommittally.

Finally, after pumping up her courage with platitudes like "nothing ventured, nothing gained" and "no guts, no glory," she did send Kyle a card, enclosing a gracefully worded message wishing him well. She wondered why she'd bothered when she received a greeting card in return that was impersonally engraved with his name. She had addressed enough such cards for her employers to know that it had been handled by his secretary as a routine matter of business. This confirmed her suspicion that only Kyle's pride had suffered when she'd declined his proposal.

One of Corey's earliest memories was of the Christmas when she was four years old. Laura Kenyon had made arrangements to see a cardiologist in Chicago only a week before Christmas that year, and when they made the trip to the city, her parents had taken Corey with them in order to show her the decorations at Marshall Field's.

She remembered how excited she'd been when her father had boosted her up to his shoulder and she'd caught her first glimpse of the store windows. She could still hear the sound of her mother's laughter, the loving note in her father's voice when he'd called her his "little grasshopper" because she was bouncing around so much, trying to take it all in.

The scene inside the window had been a workshop with a pot-bellied Santa sitting with his stockinged feet propped up on a pot-bellied stove. All around him, his elves were busily working, making toys of every imaginable description and decorating a tall Christmas tree with candies and tinsel and glittering baubles.

She could recall very little of the rest of that occasion. Although none of them had known it then, it was the last time her mother would be well enough to travel, but it had been such a happy day.

When she was older, of course, she had come to understand the religious significance of Christmas, but she still associated the holiday season with the laughter of her parents, the warmth of being part of a family, the feeling of being surrounded by love—and with that window at Marshall Field's.

To her Christmas was an evocative feast for the senses. The colors of the holiday were bright reds and greens and madonna blue and sparkling gold and silver. Its sound was laughter, and it tasted of chocolates and peppermint sticks. It was spiced with cinnamon and sage. It had the tang of oranges and cloves and the crispness of popcorn and new-fallen snow. It was redolent with the scents of pine and woodsmoke and bayberry candles.

Because it came so soon after Kyle's rebuff, this Christmas was devoid of these pleasures. Its colors were shades of gray. Its sound was a telephone that didn't ring. It was odorless, and its only taste was the bitterness of regret.

The one thing that Corey found heartening was that Jan appeared to be adapting happily to married life.

After honeymooning in the region of the Door Peninsula on Lake Michigan, the newlyweds had moved into a studio apartment they'd managed to sublet for the month or so until the fall semester began.

For a while housing presented a problem, and Jan and

Drew spent most of their time searching for a larger and more permanent residence. They haunted rental agencies and went through the classified ads in the morning and evening newspapers, but every time they investigated anything that might have been suitable they were told it had already been taken. They began to knock on the doors of apartment managers, inquiring whether any vacancies were available, attempting to get a headstart on other hopefuls.

It wasn't until mid-August, when their sublet had nearly expired and they were gloomily facing the prospect of temporarily moving in with Vera, that Lorraine and Nate came to their rescue. Since both couples preferred to live near the downtown area where Nate was going into practice with a group of obstetricians and, for the sake of Drew's convenience, near the campus, Nate proposed that the four of them take over the lease on a roomy old house that had been converted into upper and lower apartments. It was ideally situated in a quiet neighborhood off Gorham Street, near Lake Mendota and only a few blocks from Tenney Park.

Their housing problem solved, Jan threw herself into the role of homemaker. She enthusiastically occupied herself with trying out new recipes, sewing curtains and slipcovers, and restoring secondhand furniture. In their free time, Drew and some of his friends painted the apartment, covering a nondescript institutional green with sunny yellows and warm beiges. They stripped the flaking varnish from the richly carved woodwork to reveal its lustrous beauty. By the time the leaves had fallen, their first home had been transformed into a cheerfully eclectic blend of expensive wedding gifts and modern makeshift.

When Lorraine and Nate moved into the first-floor apartment after they were married in September, Jan patted her rounded belly and quipped, unknowingly prophetic, "It will be handy to have an obstetrician living just downstairs."

As Jan's pregnancy progressed, she grew closer to

Corey than she'd been before. Corey sensed that Jan was concealing qualms about her fast-approaching motherhood behind a facade of false gaiety, but by the time Christmas had come and gone and the new year began, Jan had openly reverted to intermittent outbursts of petulance.

On the first Saturday in January, Drew was trying to coax her out of a sullen mood when Jan lashed out tearfully, "You just leave me alone, Drew Zachary. If it weren't for you, I wouldn't be in this condition to begin with."

Tossing her head angrily, she threw her arms wide and cried, "Look at me! I'm as big and awkward as a cow. I can hardly climb the stairs anymore, let alone go dancing or do any of the other things I used to enjoy. I've forgotten what my feet look like, and I feel like I've been pregnant *forever*. I swear I'm going to give birth to an elephant."

"Aw, babe, you'll soon be back to normal." Drew patted her shoulder soothingly and some of the rigidity left it before he remarked, "Next time it'll be easier for you."

"Next time!" Jan shrieked, pulling away from him. "Next time!" she emphasized hotly. "If you think I'm going to go through this again, you're out of your mind!"

Jan stormed into the bedroom, slamming the door after herself, and Corey and Drew heard the sound of the lock clicking into place followed by her inconsolable sobbing. They exchanged a look of futility, and Drew pursed his lips and gave a soft whistle, wondering at his blunder.

"Boy, did I blow that one!" His voice was edged with resentment as he continued, "Jan is so damned touchy lately, she's not the only one who'll be happy when the baby comes."

Hoping to negotiate a truce, Corey said, "There's only a little more than a month to go now." When Drew remained unplacated, she added, "Jan will come around soon, you'll see. Why don't I make some coffee for all of us."

"Don't trouble yourself on my account," Drew said stiffly as he shrugged into his parka. For Jan's benefit, she called loudly in the direction of the bedroom, "I'm going down to the Student Union where my presence isn't so offensive."

After Drew's huffy departure, Corey made a cup of tea for herself and carried it through to the living room where she stood at the windows staring down into the front yard as she drank it.

So far the winter had been a mild one. There were still bare patches where the dun-colored grass showed through a thin crust of snow that was grayed by the grime of the city. For the sake of Jan and Drew, she hoped the weather would continue to be so untypically moderate. Up until now, the newlyweds had been remarkably patient with one another's flares of temper, and it was easier for Jan to remain even-tempered when she was able to get out for a daily stroll by Lake Mendota or to watch the ice skaters in the park.

Though Jan's combative mood of today was worrisome, it wasn't unexpected. In fact, it was probably a very natural reaction. After all, she was only nineteen. It couldn't be easy to stand on the sidelines and see the other girls of her age participating in all the activities she'd previously been able to engage in so effortlessly. The situation would resolve itself once the baby was safely delivered.

Smiling wryly, Corey made a wish that the baby's birth would not be overdue.

A week later, she knew her wish for a mild winter had not been granted. Madison was caught in the stranglehold of a heavy snowfall. But she got more than she'd bargained for in her second wish.

She awoke that Saturday morning to the sight of a threatening sky and an occasional fat, wet snowflake floating lazily by her window. By noon the north wind was howling fiercely and the snow had changed to icy face-stinging pellets that obscured visibility until it was impossible to see across the parking lot to the building next door.

By evening traffic in the city had come almost to a standstill. More than ten inches of snow had accumulated, several more were predicted before the storm ended, and the raging wind was piling the snow into paralyzing drifts. The plows were unable to keep up with clearing any but the major arteries, and the side streets were clogged. Here and there they were totally blocked by one or more cars that had become stuck in the snow, only to be completely buried by drifts.

By midnight the sky was clearing, although the air was filled with blowing snow as the force of the wind increased, and the temperature, already well below zero, was falling rapidly.

Corey's horoscope for that day advised her to prepare for unexpected visitors, but she had spent the day quietly, catching up on some mending and housework and writing a letter to Jill DiLoretto. She'd had a dinner date with Hal Dickinson for that evening, but he'd called to ask for a "snow check." He'd been stranded in Janesville on his way back to Madison from a visit to his parents in Rockford, Illinois.

Actually Corey was grateful for the reprieve. She liked Hal well enough, but the last few times she'd gone out with him she'd noticed troublesome signs of possessiveness creeping into his treatment of her. In an effort to let him down gently, she'd been stretching the time between their dates further and further, but instead of cooling him off this had had the opposite effect and she'd resolved to break off with him entirely the next time she saw him.

Besides, she had a new best-seller she was looking forward to reading and this seemed the perfect opportunity.

She was so immersed in the novel that she couldn't put it down. It was one o'clock in the morning before she finished it. Sighing with satisfaction, she closed the book and set it aside just as the telephone rang. Her first thought was of Jan and she rushed to answer.

"Corey? It's Drew." He sounded tired but there was an underlying ebullience in his voice.

"Is it the baby?" she asked.

"Bab*ies,*" he corrected proudly. "We have twins—a boy and a girl."

"Twins!" Her knees buckled and she collapsed onto the kitchen stool. "Twins." She savored the news a moment longer before she rushed into a torrent of speech. "Dear Lord, what a surprise! I thought they were supposed to be able to diagnose such things. You'll have to buy another layette—another one of everything! And names—what will you name them?" She paused to catch her breath. "Are Jan and the babies all right?" she asked anxiously. "Are *you* all right?"

Drew laughed at her incoherence. "Simmer down and I'll try to answer all those questions and anticipate any others you might have. Jan is fine—in fact, she's one fantastic lady! I'm fine and the babies are perfect. We're naming them Kevin and Kathleen. They were born within a few minutes of each other just after midnight. Nate delivered them here at home because the emergency vehicles couldn't get through in time. They're small—what am I saying? They're unbelievably tiny! Not quite five pounds each. But Nate says that's a lot of baby for a little thing like Jan to tote around unsuspecting all that time and it's not uncommon for twins to come prematurely. He says they're healthy." Drew chuckled. "He calls them 'keepers'!"

At that moment there was a lusty cry at the other end of the line. "Hear that! That was your nephew." Drew's voice was so filled with pride, he was nearly crowing. "I'm going to have to hang up in a minute because the ambulance has arrived and they're preparing to transfer Jan and the babies to Madison General."

"When can I see them?"

"Any time later today, I imagine. They don't restrict

visitors to specific hours on the maternity floor."

"Give my love to Jan, then, and tell her I'll see her this afternoon if I have to tunnel through the snow all the way to the hospital!"

"Will do," he agreed, chuckling at her exaggeration.

"And congratulations, Drew! This is too much to take in all at once." She laughed delightedly. "I'm not sure if I'm dreaming or awake."

" I know what you mean. I feel like I'm walking on air and I don't know when—or if—I'll come down to earth." There was a small, contented silence that Drew broke. "Look"—he spoke hurriedly—"they're ready to leave and I have to say good-bye, but before I do I wanted to ask you to do a favor for me."

"I'd be happy to."

"I've already called Vera and Maureen and I've tried several times to reach Kyle, but I keep getting a busy signal. Would you call him and give him our good news?" Taking her acquiescence for granted, Drew said hastily, "Have you a pencil? I'll give you his phone number."

Her hand was shaking so badly, the numbers she penned staggered in squiggly hentracks across the note-paper and were very nearly illegible. After Drew had hung up, she replaced the receiver carefully and glanced at the wall clock. With the time difference, on the Pacific Coast it would be a little after eleven.

There'd be no snow in San Diego, she thought numbly. It was reputed to be a paradise where "you could sleep comfortably with your windows open the year round." A technicolor paradise of palm trees, tropical skies, fragrant ocean breezes, and golden-sand beaches. And Kyle. Wherever he was would be a paradise to her.

The first time Corey dialed his number she, too, got a busy signal. She waited a few minutes—long enough to make a cup of instant coffee and take a few steadying sips of the strong, bitter brew—before she tried again. This time the call went through, but the whirring buzz of the phone ringing at the other end of the connection seemed to go on endlessly. She was about to hang up, thinking that despite the lateness of the hour Kyle must have gone out, when the phone was picked up in midring.

Her heightened senses registered the soft strains of romantic music coming over the wire. A woman's voice, familiarly accented and vaguely sulky, complained, "Kyle, darling, *must* you answer it?" and this was followed by Kyle saying crisply, "Zachary here."

"H-hello, Kyle. It's Corey Kenyon."

"You'll have to speak up." His tone was clipped and impatient. "I can hardly hear you."

There was a brief pause during which Corey tried to clear her throat. When she heard Kyle's voice again it was distant and muffled, as if he had covered the mouthpiece with his hand as he said, "For God's sake, Gillian, not now!"

"It's Corey Kenyon," she said more forcefully.

"Corey?" He sounded puzzled, almost as if he couldn't quite place the name. "Hold on a moment while I go to another phone."

The interval that followed was filled with music—all sobbing violins, throbbing jungle drums, and tinkling pianos blending in chords that were practically sweating with passion. Gillian's choice, no doubt, Corey decided spitefully. She'd expect Kyle to be less obvious, though maybe with Gillian as his partner that was exactly the sort of background music he'd select to set the mood for making love. Maybe Gillian didn't appreciate subtlety. She certainly didn't appear to be the type who would allow herself to get carried away on an inflatable lounger or be turned on by being informed she tasted of "wine and cherries and a hint of garlic."

Corey was so deep in her musings that when Kyle's voice came over the phone again she started and spilled some of her coffee onto the countertop. "You can hang up, Gillian," he instructed smoothly. "I have it here now."

Immediately there was an earsplitting retort, as if Gillian had slammed the receiver into place, then the music was gone and only an expectant silence remained.

"Well, Corey," Kyle said curtly after some moments, "are you going to tell me why you've called or do you plan to make me guess the reason?"

"I—uh—Drew asked me to phone you," she replied. "He tried to contact you himself but your line was busy and then the ambulance arrived and he had to leave for the hospital, so he couldn't keep on trying to reach you."

"Ambulance!" Kyle exclaimed sharply. "What the hell is going on back there?"

Oh, God, she was going about this all wrong, rattling on instead of telling him first thing about the babies. She inhaled deeply, making a conscious effort to calm her jangled nerves.

"P-please don't be alarmed," she stammered shakily. "They had to have the ambulance because of the snow storm, you see, but everything is fine. Really it is."

"If everything is fine," he barked the question, "why the hell did they need an ambulance in the first place?" He'd shouted so loudly that it was painful and she held the receiver a few inches away from her ear.

"I-I'm sorry. I'm doing this so badly. I guess it's because I'm so excited about the twins."

"Twins?" He was appeased by her apology and sounded mildly surprised.

"Yes." She breathed a sigh of relief that she'd found the right word at last. "Jan and Drew are the parents of twins—a boy and a girl. They were born just after twelve o'clock tonight." Hurriedly now, in a straightforward fashion, she recited the details Drew had given her.

"Twins," Kyle repeated when she had concluded, much as she had when Drew had told her, as though he were relishing the fact. "It's difficult to envision Drew as a father, let alone become accustomed to him having two children."

"I don't think he's had time to get used to the reality of it either," Corey replied. "But he told me he's walking on air, and he sounded very much the proud parent."

"You said Jan has been taken to Madison General Hospital."

"That's right."

"Then by now she's probably been admitted and I could reach them there," he commented in a preoccupied way, dismissing her.

"I'll let you go," she offered tonelessly.

"Good-bye, then," he responded with courteous indifference. "Thank you for calling."

For some minutes after she had hung up, Corey sat unmoving by the telephone. When she looked at the clock once more, she was astonished to see how little time had passed. It wasn't quite two o'clock.

It seemed appropriate somehow that in California, where Kyle was, it was still yesterday. Though she'd once played a very small part in his present and she might have shared his future, she'd foolishly thrown it all away. And now that was all he could ever represent to her. Yesterday.

CHAPTER

Fifteen

KYLE'S STAY IN San Diego lengthened from six to seven months, then extended to eight. Spring was quickening the tender green leaf buds on the trees when Drew phoned his brother to try to fix a definite date for Kevin and Kathleen's christening.

After he'd talked to Kyle, Drew reported to Jan and Corey, "I told him his niece and nephew are growing so fast, if he doesn't make it to Madison soon, he'll have missed out entirely on their infancy. They'll be toddlers."

"What did Kyle say to that?" Jan asked eagerly.

"That he'd like to see the babies, although we've sent him enough snapshots that he could paper his walls with them, so at times he feels he *has*."

Jan broke in impatiently, "But did he agree to come, or what?"

"He agreed, all right, but I had to pull out all the stops to get him to. It seems they've run into one snag after another with the last store they opened. He said he'd hate to see the twins go unbaptized till they've reached puberty and suggested that we go ahead without him, but I told him, 'no way!' and threatened to really lay the guilt on him if he didn't juggle his schedule so he can be here sometime in the next few weeks." Chuckling, Drew confided, "I even threatened not to send him any more pictures of the babies!"

"That must have been what cinched it," Jan said in a teasing tone of voice.

These days Drew practically lived with a camera in his hands. He'd photographed the babies eating and sleeping, crying and smiling, in their baths, in their carriage, and at every conceivable time of the day or night. He was likely to pop out with his camera at some of the most ungodly hours and start clicking away when Jan least expected it.

Casually, as if the answer was only of passing interest to her, Corey asked, "When will you have the christening?"

"We settled on the Sunday following Easter," said Drew. "Kyle's going to clear his appointments so he'll be able to arrive in Madison Saturday evening. He won't be able to stay long, though. He'll be returning to California on a late-afternoon flight on Sunday."

Now that they had succeeded in getting Kyle to commit himself to a specific date, Jan and Drew turned their attentions to Corey. They told her in no uncertain terms how puzzling they found her strange reluctance to be named as Kevin's godmother.

"Honestly, Corey," Jan exclaimed in disgust one evening when Corey had been drafted as a babysitter for the afternoon and had stayed to have dinner with them, "I don't understand why you're being so pigheaded about this. I should think you'd be *honored*."

"I am honored that you've asked me, Jan, but it's not a responsibility to assume lightly," Corey said. "I'm just not sure I want to take it on."

"But you *adore* the babies! You know you do! You're the original doting auntie to Kevin and Katy. Is it that your feelings are hurt because we approached you last, or some silly thing like that?"

Before Corey could respond, Jan rushed on, "You know there was a perfectly valid reason why we felt it would be better to line up Maureen, Mitch, and Kyle first. I mean, you're right here in town, so it's sensible to believe it would be easier for you to rearrange your schedule to conform to their convenience if there were any conflict. We never thought that *you*, of all people, would quibble over this."

Sighing, Corey said, "It's nothing like that."

"Well, I certainly wish you'd tell us why you won't agree to do it. The excuses you've given so far just don't ring true." Shaking her head, Jan began stacking the dinner plates onto a tray, preparing to serve dessert. As she backed through the swinging door into the kitchen, she delivered a parting accusation.

"From the way you and Kyle have been behaving, if I didn't know better, I'd say you were trying to avoid each other. The two of you are acting as if you're ex-lovers or something!"

The door swung shut behind Jan as she finished speaking, so she had no chance to notice Corey's sudden pallor, but Drew did.

"My God! That's it, isn't it? You and Kyle are— Dammit all anyway, Corey! What the hell were you thinking of? I warned you about Kyle. I thought you had more common sense."

"I'm afraid common sense doesn't enter into it, Drew," she replied in a low voice, "but I'm sorry I've disillusioned you."

"Hey, hold on a minute! I'm the one who should apologize. Last summer you did all you could to help Jan and me, and you never once judged us, and here I am acting the heavy-handed father. It's my big brother I'm really mad at. Much as I admire the guy, I'd like to punch him out for hurting you."

"It wasn't the way you're thinking, Drew. Kyle asked me to marry him."

"And you turned him down?"

Corey nodded.

"But why? From your expression it's obvious you're still all torn up over it, even after all this time. You've really fallen for him, haven't you?"

"I'm in love with Kyle," she replied haltingly. "At the time I thought I had a good reason for refusing, but now—" She faltered into silence and concentrated very hard on the stained-glass intaglio hanging in the window behind Drew in order to keep from crying.

"Unless you want to create a family rift, you'll have to see Kyle sooner or later," Drew pointed out gently. "I'm sorry as hell about this whole situation, and if you say no, I promise you that Jan and I won't pressure you any more, but I think you should agree to being Kevin's godmother."

At last, Corey gave in to her desire to see Kyle again and bowed to the inevitable.

It was a particularly happy time for Jan and Drew. They'd come safely through the hardest period of adjustment to married life, the twins were thriving, and Drew had completed the requirements for his doctorate. On the strength of his dissertation, he had secured a position on the faculty of a small but prestigious private college in Beloit. His degree was to be conferred at the spring graduation exercises, and in the interim before he took up his teaching post late in the summer, he said he planned to enjoy his family and his music, in that order.

For all these reasons, but mostly because they enjoyed entertaining spontaneously, they decided to have a party in celebration of their good fortune on the Saturday evening before the twins' christening. All of Drew's family would be in town, and they could invite their friends from the university, Corey, Lorraine and Nate, and, of course, Vera.

Jan made no secret of the fact that she derived a good deal of her enjoyment of these occasions from asking such a volatile mix of guests to her home. Sometimes it proved explosive, sometimes it turned out to be an innocuous blend, but it was never boring.

When she phoned to invite Corey, Jan promised her that this party would be casual and fun, with Drew and his band providing live music to add variety to their large collection of taped music.

"I'll probably serve something really simple, like wine, cheese, and crackers," Jan said thoughtfully. "Of course, with the crowd from college, I'll have to have plenty of beer on hand, too. If the twins are good that day, maybe I'll have time to prepare some more elaborate canapes—but nothing too time consuming."

Jan believed that being the hostess shouldn't stand in the way of her having a good time at the party.

Things turned out pretty much as Jan had planned. The only possible problem was that Hal came to the party more than a little the worse for drink and was making a nuisance of himself with Corey.

"I can see why he's tempted to be such a pest," Drew complimented his sister-in-law. "You're looking especially fetching tonight."

Corey hoped she *did* look her best. She had certainly tried to. Her mirror had told her that the midnight-blue jumpsuit she was wearing was flattering. It left the creamy skin of her arms and shoulders bare, turned her eyes to the color of violets, and faithfully hugged the shapely contours of her body.

She knew to the second when Kyle walked into the room. But even if she hadn't sensed his presence, the envious looks that were cast in Jan's direction by the women guests would have told her that Kyle had arrived.

He was dashing and dominant and even better looking than she had remembered in light-gray slacks and a charcoal kidskin jacket that was perfectly tailored to the athletic proportions of his broad shoulders and lean waist.

Kyle greeted Jan fondly, giving her a brotherly kiss on the cheek before she took him into Kevin and Katy's room for his first view of the sleeping babies. When they rejoined the party, Corey thought that his praise for his niece and nephew must have been enthusiastic enough to satisfy even Jan, because she was content to let Drew, Maureen, and Mitch monopolize his attention while she looked on.

Jan seemed to be amused by the number of her friends who were trying to appear nonchalant about having gravitated to the fringes of the Zachary family group. Despite his put-down of her last summer, even Vera, who was still in a state of shock at finding herself a grandmother twice over, was avidly waiting to renew her acquaintance with Kyle.

The painful irony that she was the only woman at the party who seemed to be immune to Kyle's appeal was not lost on Corey. She felt it intensely, although she stayed on the far side of the room, dancing with Nate and trying to avoid Hal, who was showing symptoms he might become distressingly obnoxious before the evening was over.

But all the while she was dancing, Corey was surreptitiously watching Kyle over Nate's shoulder and aching for the feel of Kyle's arms around her. She was an idiot to have come to Jan's party, but she'd been unable to stay away.

Her absorption with Kyle accounted for the fact that, only a short time later, Hal caught her off guard. Otherwise she would have remained alert and managed to continue eluding him. As it was, she found herself trapped into dancing with him. He held her much too close and, in spite of the fast tempo of the music, once he'd maneuvered her into a dimly lighted corner, he hardly moved except for his questing hands.

At first she tried to disengage herself without causing a scene. Then, as his advances became more and more aggressive and his arms forged a steely prison about her, as his hands sought to take greater liberties, she panicked and stamped hard on his instep with the spiked heel of her shoe. When he doubled over in pained reaction, she freed herself.

Before she could make good her escape, however, Hal had recovered. Grasping her by the arm with frightening strength, he brought his leering face close to hers and muttered drunkenly, "C'mon, Corey, baby! Let me take you home now." His mouth was contorted by a slack-lipped smile that was very nearly obscene. "We don't need all these people around us to have a good time."

"Please, let me go, Hal," she cajoled him. "I don't want to leave just yet."

"First you have to promise you'll let me take you home. You don't know how much I've missed you, baby."

He pulled her close again and Corey was bordering on actual fear when Kyle's voice came cuttingly from behind her.

"Let her go, Hal," he ordered coldly. "You're too drunk to drive yourself anywhere, let alone take Corey home."

"What's it to you, Zachary?" Hal snarled belligerently. "It's none of your damned business if Corey wants to come with me. This is a private matter between the two of us, so butt out!"

In response, Kyle's hand shot out and gripped Hal, pincerlike, at one side of the base of his neck. As his fingers tightened, biting into the muscle with tensile strength, he repeated with quiet assurance, "I said let her go, Hal."

No sooner had she been released from Hal's restricting hold than she became a captive of Kyle's. With his hands on her shoulders, he held her close and danced her into the better lighted but deserted foyer before setting her slightly away from him in order to subject her to the piercing exploration of his dark eyes. His gaze lingered at the decolletage of her jumpsuit, on the curve of her breasts and the shadowy valley between them. His eyes were an aphrodisiac for Corey and her breasts seemed to swell until they strained the soft material covering them.

Suddenly Kyle's arms circled her completely, looping about her so that her arms were pinioned at her sides.

"You're not letting Dickinson drive you home," he said huskily. "He's so far out of it, he'd better sleep it off here before he goes anywhere. *I'll* take you home."

"Oh, but—"

"I don't give a damn what your objections are, I'm taking you home!"

A small smile of satisfaction touched the corners of her mouth and she turned her face aside to conceal it from Kyle. She had intended only to protest that she'd brought herself to the party and that her own car was parked just down the block, but she could ride the bus here tomorrow and pick it up after the christening. Since his plan to drive her home coincidsd with her own wishes, she nodded and murmured docilely, "Yes, Kyle."

Moving closer to him, she slipped her arms inside his jacket and wrapped them around his waist. Her fingertips moved hungrily over his back when she felt the supple warmth of his skin through the fine fabric of his shirt.

Kyle's hands were following the length of her spine in a cherishing caress from shoulder to hip. His touch was so light that the provocative up-and-down stroking had been repeated several times before she became fully aware of it. But once she was, she found that she was the hostage of her own inflamed senses.

She was a hostage to the sultry sound of Drew's clarinet, backed only by the bass as the combo played the refrain of a hauntingly romantic ballad. She was a hostage to the racing counterpoint of her heartbeat. She was captivated by the intoxicating mingling of Kyle's aftershave with the leather of his jacket and his unique male scent, by the slow fire of his mouth as it moved across her temple, by the faint rasp of his beard as he rubbed his cheek against hers. She was bound to Kyle by the frank eroticism of his hands on her.

Without warning his grip on her hardened, his hands at the small of her back roughly molding her softness to the taut length of his thighs, and she knew that the urgency of his need matched her own.

"Let's get out of here," he said gruffly.

They collected her evening bag from the hall table, but they didn't look for her coat or stop to say good night to Jan and Drew. Kyle simply guided her down the stairs and out into the starry crispness of the April dark.

Perhaps the chill temperature of the early spring night had a sobering effect on him that caused the sudden remoteness of his manner toward her.

When he'd handed her into his rented sedan, he observed coolly, "Last summer you'd never have joined in a party as you did tonight. You'd have been hiding out in the kitchen or watching from some quiet corner. You've changed, Corey, and I wonder why and how much."

Her breathing was short and shallow as she countered, "Since you're taking me home, maybe you'll have the opportunity to find out."

His narrowed glance raked over her, but because of the shadowy interior of the car she could only sense his scorn as he conducted a detached appraisal of her because of that invitation she had given him.

He turned away from her abruptly, started the engine, and pulled sharply away from the curb. His aloof silence and the way in which he drummed his fingers on the wheel at each stoplight as he drove across the Isthmus toward her apartment communicated that he was either impatient or angry—probably both. She felt cold and abandoned and shivered as he swung into the parking lot of her building.

Kyle didn't turn the key in the ignition. He left the motor idling as he reached in front of her to open her door. As he drew it back, his arm brushed against her breasts and she shivered again.

"Won't you come in for coffee?" she asked shakily.

Moving deliberately, Kyle switched the engine off and turned to face her. He sat with one arm stretched along the seat back behind her and, as he studied her, the nearby light in the parking lot fell fully on her while he was in dim shadow.

"I've no doubt you'll make it worth my while if I do come in," he drawled.

Curving his arm around her shoulders, Kyle slid her toward him along the slippery leather of the upholstery.

His hand was scorchingly hot against the coolness of her skin. When he had tucked her close to his side, his other hand took possession of the tab on the zip-fastener at the front of her jumpsuit.

He fiddled lazily with the zipper, moving it fractionally up and down its track several times before he decisively pulled it down several inches and slipped his hand inside to cover her breast. With exquisite slowness, he insinuated one finger into the lacy cup of her bra and teased the nipple to tautness. Only then did he nod slightly, as if he were satisfied with her reaction, and withdraw his hand.

As he settled the zipper back into place, he said brusquely, "What are we waiting for? Let's go inside. I've discovered I have a craving for . . . coffee."

She was flayed by the insolence in his tone. Her mind was racing as frantically as her pulse as she fumbled in her bag for her key.

Had Kyle thought she would change her mind? Didn't he realize that it was too late now for her to turn back? Surely he must know that she loved him so deeply she had no choice but to accept whatever he offered.

At last she found the key and handed it to Kyle. He unlocked the door and swung it wide for her to precede him and she stepped inside, automatically reaching for the light switch. But with predatory quickness, he stopped her, catching her wrist with one hand while the other closed the door behind them. In spite of the Stygian darkness, he turned the deadbolt and found the chain. She heard him slide it home.

"We don't need any lights," he said harshly as he moved closer to her, pinning her against the wall with his body, "and we don't need any coffee."

His hands moved to clamp either side of her head in a viselike grip and his mouth came down on hers with grinding savagery, bruising the softness of her lips against the barrier of her teeth before they parted to admit the greedy plundering of his tongue.

If his kiss was a punishment, his hands were an insult.

They ravished her, tormenting her with their roughness as they carelessly claimed the tender fullness of her breasts. She was so lightheaded and dizzy that she felt he was forcing all the breath from her body as he crushed her between the wall and the hard thrust of his hips.

Had she hurt him so much, then, that he would want to strike back by treating her so hatefully—that he should treat her as if she were a tramp?

"Sometimes when a person is behaving the least lovably, it's an indication they need more love than ever." Corey was despairing when, as if she were hallucinating, some small corner of her mind recalled Anson quoting her mother. While she couldn't truly respond to Kyle's handling her this way, she also couldn't deny him because she sensed that his desperation rivaled her own. She remained malleable in his arms, submitting to his will, allowing him to do what he would with her.

Was it her tears that gentled him? Although she felt she was weeping on the inside, mourning for what might have been, she hadn't known she was crying until she tasted the saltiness of tears. And in that moment of awareness, the quality of Kyle's embrace changed from impersonal lust to infinite tenderness.

A low moan escaped him, and he rested his cheek against hers before he buried his face in the curve of her neck.

She wanted so much to comfort him. Her hand wove its way through his hair and strayed to his cheek. When she encountered the dampness of his tears there, she paused in amazement.

"You know this is no good, don't you, Corey?" Kyle pressed the palm of her hand to his lips before he pushed her away from him. "I guess the last laugh is on me, because it's obvious that I want you," he whispered raggedly. "From the first time I saw you, I've wanted you as I've never wanted any other woman. But even when I try to pretend you're someone else, it just won't work. I can't forget it's you I'm holding, and I can't bring myself to settle for an occasional night with you."

Corey realized he had turned away from her and was unlocking the door.

"Please, Kyle," she pleaded huskily, "don't leave."

"Dammit, Corey! Don't make this any tougher than it already is."

He had opened the door and although the rest of the room was still shrouded in darkness, she blinked rapidly as the light from the hallway spilled in, bathing her face with brightness and momentarily blinding her.

Dear God, he was leaving, and she couldn't just stand there and do nothing while he walked out of her life.

"Since you feel so strongly about it," she called to his back as he walked through the doorway, "would it make any difference if I asked you to marry me?"

She held her breath when she saw the stillness that overtook him, the tension in his clenched fist.

"Is that a hypothetical question?" he asked softly, and she closed her eyes in a silent prayer of thanksgiving at this proof that he also remembered every word of their last conversation on the topic of marriage.

Her voice was tremulous with emotion as she replied, "No, it's a serious question. I'm asking you to marry me, Kyle."

Although he remained with his back to her, his hand gradually relaxed. Slowly he turned to face her.

"Do you love me?"

"Yes! Oh, yes, I love you." She rejoiced in finally saying the words to him. "Oh, Kyle, I love you so very much!"

Kyle held out his arms to her, and the loving warmth of his smile as she ran into them dispelled the last of the doubt between them.

"Darling Corey," he whispered as he gathered her close, "I thought you'd never ask. I'd be delighted and honored to marry you." His voice was unsteady as he added, "I should warn you, though, that even starting on the project right this minute, it will take me the rest of our lives to show you how happy you've made me."

"And I should warn you," she said shyly, "that both of my grandmothers were twins."

His arms tightened about her and he laughed deep in his throat. "If that's a promise, I intend to hold you to it."

"And I intend to hold you to yours."

He raised his head to smile down at her. "About taking the rest of our lives?"

Corey nodded. "And about starting this minute."

For long moments, their eyes met in a silent exchange of vows. Then Kyle growled seductively, "Try and stop me."

He closed and locked the door unhurriedly, as if he knew they had all the time in the world, but they were shedding their clothes even while he led her toward the bedroom, leaving an intimate trail that proclaimed their urgency. And in the bedroom, Kyle turned on all the lights before they finished undressing each other.

When Corey lay beside him, her shyness forgotten, lovely and proud in her nakedness, he adored her with his eyes, with his hands, with his lips, until they were both trembling with desire and he covered her body with his.

She received him joyfully, meeting his demands with her own eager movements, pleasuring him and taking the pleasure he gave her with an artless abandon that told Kyle how completely she trusted him. And from the first moment of his possession, she experienced an ecstasy so sweet, so profound, that it was very nearly painful.

Her eyes wide with wonder, she looked up at Kyle and saw that his eyes mirrored her own rapture, and in the very instant her body embraced him fully, Corey saw herself and all the bright promise of their future together in his eyes. In that instant the sweetness reached its peak and she cried out at the beauty of it, but he silenced her cries with his lips. Withholding nothing, she gave herself to him so generously that he accepted the gift of love she offered with a passion that was almost reverent.

Afterward Kyle held Corey in his arms and they talked in contented whispers, making plans for their wedding, for where they would honeymoon when Kyle's work in San Diego was finished, and where they would live after that.

At one point Corey said softly, "Inside I feel just like—well, like it's *Christmas!* You were right, Kyle. Making love *is* beautiful."

Kyle chuckled but his voice was hushed and solemn as he replied, "My darling Corey, until I met you, I never knew *how* beautiful."

He vetoed her suggestion that they have a church wedding, saying lightly, "Oh, no you don't, young lady. If you want a big, formal wedding you're out of luck—unless you'll settle for one on our fiftieth anniversary! I've got you where I want you now, and I'm not about to let you go. When I leave here tomorrow, you're coming with me. We'll stop over in Las Vegas, and twenty-four hours from now you'll be my wife *legally!*"

Laughing at his adamance, Corey teased, "I thought you weren't ready to put your neck in the marriage noose."

"That was before I'd had time to consider the advantages of having a sexy little witch like you for my wife. Then I thought, 'What a way to go!'"

Hugging her even closer to him, Kyle kissed her and murmured, "You're mine, Corey, and you always will be."

They did no more talking for quite a while after that. Instead Kyle made love to her again with a breathtaking intensity that left both of them langorous with fulfillment.

Much later, Corey fought to stay awake. She wanted to slow the passage of time so that she might distill every atom of delight from the happenings of the night.

Even while he slept, Kyle held her in his arms. It was as if he couldn't bear to let her go, and she found the intimacy of his possessive hold utterly delicious. When he held her she had a sensation of being safely encompassed by love that was very like the way she'd felt when she was a little girl perched on her father's shoulder, looking into the window at Marshall Field's. In a way it was the same as the cozy feeling she'd had on that long-ago day, but it was infinitely more wonderful. Just being close to Kyle was heavenly.

Oddly enough, she also felt very close to her mother. She had a mystical feeling that somehow, somewhere, Laura Kenyon was approving of the woman her daughter had become and smiling a blessing on her union with Kyle.

Although Corey knew she might have to wait a long time before Kyle would tell her he loved her, this knowledge did nothing to diminish her happiness. He might not say he loved her until they were old and gray. Perhaps he would never actually say the words. But that was of no importance, because she *knew* he did, and she knew that his love was as warm and strong and enduring as his arms around her.

With his eyes, with his smile and his kisses, with the touch of his hands and with the passionate eloquence of his body, Kyle had said it all.

WATCH FOR
6 NEW TITLES EVERY MONTH!

Second Chance at Love

____ 05703-7 **FLAMENCO NIGHTS #1** Susanna Collins

____ 05637-5 **WINTER LOVE SONG #2** Meredith Kingston

____ 05624-3 **THE CHADBOURNE LUCK #3** Lucia Curzon

____ 05777-0 **OUT OF A DREAM #4** Jennifer Rose

____ 05878-5 **GLITTER GIRL #5** Jocelyn Day

____ 05863-7 **AN ARTFUL LADY #6** Sabina Clark

____ 05694-4 **EMERALD BAY #7** Winter Ames

____ 05776-2 **RAPTURE REGAINED #8** Serena Alexander

____ 05801-7 **THE CAUTIOUS HEART #9** Philippa Heywood

____ 05907-2 **ALOHA YESTERDAY #10** Meredith Kingston

____ 05638-3 **MOONFIRE MELODY #11** Lily Bradford

____ 06132-8 **MEETING WITH THE PAST #12** Caroline Halter

____ 05623-5 **WINDS OF MORNING #13** Laurie Marath

____ 05704-5 **HARD TO HANDLE #14** Susanna Collins

____ 06067-4 **BELOVED PIRATE #15** Margie Michaels

____ 05978-1 **PASSION'S FLIGHT #16** Marilyn Mathieu

____ 05847-5 **HEART OF THE GLEN #17** Lily Bradford

____ 05977-3 **BIRD OF PARADISE #18** Winter Ames

____ 05705-3 **DESTINY'S SPELL #19** Susanna Collins

____ 06106-9 **GENTLE TORMENT #20** Johanna Phillips

____ 06059-3 **MAYAN ENCHANTMENT #21** Lila Ford

____ 06301-0 **LED INTO SUNLIGHT #22** Claire Evans

____ 06131-X **CRYSTAL FIRE #23** Valerie Nye

____ 06150-6 **PASSION'S GAMES #24** Meredith Kingston

____ 06160-3 **GIFT OF ORCHIDS #25** Patti Moore

____ 06108-5 **SILKEN CARESSES #26** Samantha Carroll

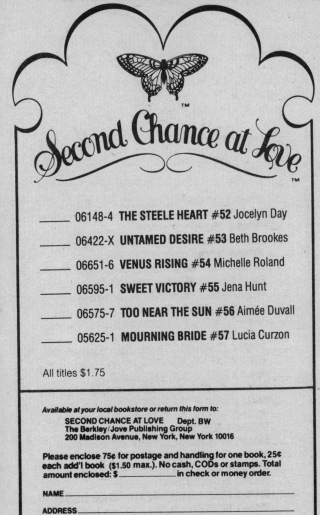

WHAT READERS SAY ABOUT
SECOND CHANCE AT LOVE

"SECOND CHANCE AT LOVE is fantastic."
—*J. L., Greenville, South Carolina**

"SECOND CHANCE AT LOVE has all the romance of the big novels."
—*L. W., Oak Grove, Missouri**

"You deserve a standing ovation!"
—*S. C., Birch Run, Michigan**

"Thank you for putting out this type of story. Love and passion have no time limits. I look forward to more of these good books."
—*E. G., Huntsville, Alabama**

"Thank you for your excellent series of books. Our book stores receive their monthly selections between the second and third week of every month. Please believe me when I say they have a frantic female calling them every day until they get your books in."
—*C. Y., Sacramento, California**

"I have become addicted to the SECOND CHANCE AT LOVE books...You can be very proud of these books....I look forward to them each month."
—*D. A., Floral City, Florida**

"I have enjoyed every one of your SECOND CHANCE AT LOVE books. Reading them is like eating potato chips, once you start you just can't stop."
—*L. S., Kenosha, Wisconsin**

"I consider your SECOND CHANCE AT LOVE books the best on the market."
—*D. S., Redmond, Washington**

*Names and addresses available upon request